RECIPES FOR CHAMPIONS

WATCH OUR EASY STEP-BY-STEP VIDEO RECIPE TUTORIALS!

How can you watch the recipe tutorials?

1. Download the free Layar app on your smartphone or Android device OR scan the QR Code below to access the Layar app.

2. Scan a photo of the recipe.

3. The video will appear on your smartphone or device.

4. Click play.

5. Watch!

www.recipesforchampions.com

RECIPES FOR CHAMPIONS

50 EASY RECIPES TO MAXIMIZE PERFORMANCE
NORMAL TRAINING, MUSCLE MASS BUILDING,
COMPETITION, RECOVERY

Dr. Philippe Kuentz
Andrea Mäusli
Eléonore Schoettel
Eve Tiollier
Tara Ostrowe

Sport @ Food @ Health

Nutrition and energy plays a major role in sports performance.

Athletes know the value of a healthy, varied diet, adapted to their sport.

In order to put this theory into practice, however, a step is missing – the creation of recipes that follow the major dietary guidelines for performance and health.

Created specifically for sports practitioners, this cookbook aims to help athletes of all levels – along with their families – cook food that is delicious, healthy, easy to prepare, and that respects the dietary guidelines of their sport. The recipes are very simple to prepare, and the success of a dish is guaranteed.

Short videos showcasing the main steps of each recipe are available online.

After a brief section explaining the basics of sports nutrition, you will find approximately 50 recipes, all validated by our nutritionists. Moreover, each recipe contains hints and tips to ease preparation.

You can select your meal according to your athletic goals, type of workout, and weight, among other parameters.

ENJOY YOUR TRAINING, YOUR COMPETITION, YOUR RECOVERY, AND, ESPECIALLY, YOUR MEAL.

Dr. Philippe Kuentz

IN THIS BOOK, YOU WILL DISCOVER HOW TO CREATE A BALANCED AND DELICIOUS DIET, PERFECT FOR HEALTH AND ATHLETIC PERFORMANCE.

All recipes are categorized by food group.

Each recipe's main characteristics are showcased in easy-to-understand icons; some dishes can be used for different activities.
Each recipe makes two servings, with each serving suitable for a person weighing approx. 155 lb. (70 kg). The nutritional content listed is per single serving.
A short video, presenting the various stages of preparation, from set-up to cooking, is available for most recipes online.

To be effective, an athletic diet must also be a pleasure – a pleasure to eat, to discover, and to feel your best. These recipes are delicious, appetizing, varied, and effective.
Mealtime is a special time. Sitting comfortably at a table and relaxing – eating together is essential for building cohesion in a group, as well as in a team.

 Carbohydrates per serving

 Particularly high in micronutrients, minerals, and vitamins

 Gluten free

 Ideal for rest and recovery. Rapid food intake, shortly after exercise

 Ideal for normal training and daily workouts throughout the season

 Protein per serving

 On event day, prioritize: hydration, ease of digestion, and glycogen reserves

 Ideal for weight loss, low in calories

 Fat per serving

 Energy per serving, expressed in calories

 Ideal for intense training, high RPE levels, start of the season. Needs are increased to meet energy expenditure.

 Ideal for muscle mass building

CONTENTS

INTRODUCTION

NUTRITION

PREPARATION

MEAL PLANNING

RECIPES

ADDITIONAL INFORMATION

NUTRITION IS ESSENTIAL FOR CHAMPIONS

Sophie Herbrecht
World Handball Champion

"Success starts on the plate, **EATING WELL IS THE KEY TO SUCCESS!**"

Radamel Falcao
Colombian Soccer Player, AS Monaco Forward

"NUTRITION IS A KEY PART OF ATHLETIC PERFORMANCE."

Kevin Boothe
New York Giants Super Bowl Winner, Winner of the Vince Lombardi Super Bowl Trophy

"FUELING WITH THE BEST FOODS provided the strength and endurance to block my opponents throughout entire games."

Caroline Wozniacki
Danish Professional Tennis Player

"To me **NUTRITION IS VERY IMPORTANT.** To perform my best, I need to put the right fuel into my body! It's like if you have the best car in the world, but put the wrong fuel in it, it's not going to go very far. It's the same principle in the body of an athlete."

Ibrahim Sekagya
New York Red Bulls Assistant Coach

"I always followed **A CLEAN AND BALANCED DIET** to provide the energy needed to stay fit, play at a top level, and train well."

Paula Radcliffe
World Champion and Women's World Record Holder in Marathon with a time of 2:15:25

"If we want to succeed, we have to respect our body and provide it with fuel. By eating a good, balanced diet, our bodies will respond, and we have a better chance of achieving our goals. **EATING WELL IS A PLEASURE!**"

Tomas Berdych
Professional Tennis Player

"Dear reader,
My name is Tomas Berdych. I am a professional tennis player, ranked in the Top 10 for many years. Many aspects of a professional life need special attention. Diet is one of them. It is important to get carbohydrates and proteins in the right amounts to be able to perform when needed – but you also have to be aware when to eat what. 'Recipes for Champions' will help you put together the right meals at the right time. **ENJOY YOUR FOOD AS MUCH AS I DO!**"

Julien Absalon
Cross-Country Mountain Bike Double Olympic Champion, Five-Time World Champion

"NUTRITION IS AN IMPORTANT PARAMETER IN ALL ENDURANCE SPORTS.

Good nutrition helps regulate body weight – the power-to-weight ratio is important in endurance sports – but also assists in recuperating rapidly after exercise, as well as optimizing energy efficiency and preventing deficiencies in nutrients. "

Djibril Sidibe
International French Soccer Player, AS Monaco Defender

"WATER AND ORGANIC FOODS, A PERFECT COMBINATION! I am very careful with my food intake. It's essential for an athlete."

Ricardo Carvalho
Portuguese International Soccer Player, European Champion 2016

"FOOD MAKES THE DIFFERENCE! GOOD FOOD, GOOD LIFE."

Thibaut Pinot
Professional Cyclist, Team FDJ

Mathias Wibault
Member of the French Cross-Country Ski Team

Anouk Faivre Picon
Member of the French Cross-Country Ski Team

"NUTRITION HOLDS A PLACE OF UTMOST IMPORTANCE IN OUR FIELD OF PROFESSIONAL CYCLING.
Our choice of food is essential, both for energy, as well as for nutrition, resistance, and staying healthy – which is indispensable for peak performance."

"Can you perform in a sport without giving the body the nutrients necessary for regeneration? Impossible! In cross-country skiing, a large amount of energy is expended, due to the nature of the discipline and its harsh conditions. **GOOD NUTRITION IS VITAL!"**

"FOR ME AND MY SPORT, GOOD NUTRITION MUST BE HEALTHY, DIVERSE, AND SEASONAL, BUT, MOST IMPORTANTLY, IT MUST BE AN ABSOLUTE PLEASURE...
Cook and eat, while acknowledging the benefits of each food."

SCIENTIFIC ADVICE AND INFORMATION

WHAT IS SPORTS NUTRITION?

Nutrition must provide enough energy for exercise and replenishing reserves.

An athlete's total daily energy intake should exceed 2,000 calories a day.

An individual's weight should be taken into account when considering caloric needs. For normal training, an athlete requires between 16-23 calories per pound of body weight a day, or 35-50 kcal per kg a day. During high intensity training, a sportsperson needs up to 25 calories per pound of body weight a day, or 55 kcal per kg a day.

Naturally, there are variations, depending on the type of sport, the level of practice, the duration of exercise, environmental conditions, and gender, among others. A purely energy-based approach is insufficient for an athlete.

An athlete also requires **macronutrients**, such as protein, carbohydrates, and fat, which must be spread out properly throughout their daily meals. **Micronutrients** – also known as vitamins, minerals, and antioxidants – are also necessary for an active lifestyle.
Micronutrients contain neither energy, nor calories, yet are essential for the proper functioning of the organism.
The goal is to cover all these nutritional requirements by monitoring the **variety** and **quality** of one's food intake.

The diet should be separated into a minimum of four meals a day: breakfast; two main meals; and at least one healthy snack.
Food intake should be adapted to different types of training, as well as for pre- and post-competition.
When implemented properly, nutrition optimizes athletic performance and promotes good health.

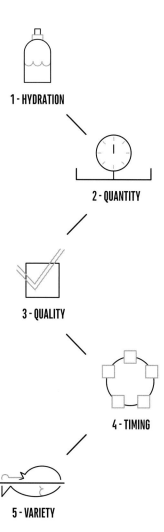

1 - HYDRATION

2 - QUANTITY

3 - QUALITY

4 - TIMING

5 - VARIETY

PROTEIN

WHAT IS IT?

Protein is made up of a chain of amino acids that help build and renew cells in the body, particularly the muscles. There is a difference between animal and vegetable protein.

WHERE TO FIND IT?

1/ Animal Protein

Animal protein is mostly found in meats, fish, eggs, and dairy. The best meat choices are tenderloin cuts of veal, beef and pork, as well as poultry, venison, bison and rabbit. Whenever possible, always select the leanest cuts and remove the skin. It is important to vary protein sources, as all meats have pros and cons, and contain different nutrients.
It is recommended to consume a variety of fish at least two-to-three times a week. The most preferable choices are wild, deep-sea fish, rich in Omega-3 and other cardio-protective agents, such as albacore tuna, salmon, mackerel, and sardines. Other ideal fish choices for an athlete are cod or sole – noteworthy as sources of protein – and squid or shrimp, which are low in fat. Mussels are also a superb option, as they are particularly high in iron.

Eggs

Egg white is low in calories and high in protein, while the yolk contains fat, calories and iron, as well as vitamin D and B vitamins. One can consume 6-8 eggs per week.

Dairy

In terms of dairy, skim or 1% fat products are preferred. Dairy products contain B vitamins, vitamin A, vitamin D, calcium, potassium, phosphorus, and magnesium, which are all indispensable for intense physical activity. Dairy is also beneficial for exercise recovery. It is recommended to limit cheese consumption, as it is often high in fat.

2/ Vegetable Protein

Vegetable protein is found in: legumes, such as beans, lentils, and peas; grains, including wheat, rice, and oats; and leafy greens. Vegetable protein is generally considered lesser quality than animal-based sources.

Combining legumes and grains is essential, since each food completes the other's deficits, leading to a better quality protein. A high fiber content aids digestion, while B-group vitamins strengthen neurotransmitters and immunity.

WHAT IS ITS ROLE?

Protein is needed for building muscle, which makes it very important for physical activity. Combining protein with carbohydrates improves recovery and muscle repair. Protein also plays an important role in a multitude of other functions, such as immunity, development, energy, intra-
cellular communication, and the facilitation of biochemical reactions within the body.

HOW MUCH DO YOU NEED?

Protein requirements are calculated depending on body weight. Average activity requires .68g of protein per pound of body weight a day, or 1.5 g of protein per kg a day. Increasing muscle mass needs 1g of protein per pound of body weight a day, or 2.2 g of protein per kg a day. It is recommended that protein powder supplements do not exceed one-third of daily protein intake. These numbers do not correspond to the weight of the food, but to the quantity of protein contained in the food.
Example : A 3.5 oz. (100 g) chicken breast contains 25 g of protein.

REQUIREMENTS CAN VARY

Requirements vary depending on the type of sport. Endurance sports require between .6-.7 g per pound of body weight a day, or 1.4-1.6 g per kg a day. During muscle mass building and pre-season practice, as well as with sports that require short, intense bursts of effort, protein recommendations increase to .9 g per pound of body weight a day, or 2 g per kg a day. In the event of injury, protein needs increase to between .8g-1g per pound of body weight a day, or 1.7-2.5 g per kg a day.

CARBOHYDRATES

WHAT ARE THEY?

Carbohydrates are composed of sugar, in all its forms.

WHERE TO FIND THEM?

Carbohydrates can be found in: starches, such as bread, potatoes, rice, quinoa, and legumes; fruits; and sugar products, including pastries, honey, syrup, candy, chocolate, sodas, and sugary drinks.
Legumes are noteworthy for their vitamin, mineral, and fiber content, and should be consumed at least twice a week.

WHAT IS THEIR ROLE ?

Carbohydrates provide fuel, stored as glycogen in the liver and muscles. This fuel powers intense activity. When glycogen reserves are depleted, energy production relies on fat. In this situation, a person is often incapable of sustaining intense activity.
An excess of carbohydrates facilitates the storage of energy in the form of fat.

HOW MUCH DO YOU NEED?

The recommended daily allowance for carbohydrates varies, depending on a number of factors, such as: size, training load, type of sport, and weight management.
Light training requires 1.4g per pound of body weight a day, or
3 g per kg a day. Heavy training or competition needs 4.5 g per pound of body weight a day, or 10 g per kg a day.

So-called "good carbs" have a low glycemic index, and are particularly beneficial, since they do not spike blood-sugar levels.

Cooking and preparation can greatly alter the glycemic index of carbohydrate-rich foods. For example, if overcooked, a particular pasta will contain a high glycemic index, while the same pasta cooked "al dente" will have a low glycemic index.

REQUIREMENTS CAN VARY

Carbohydrate intake should be higher the day before competition, or when competition is carried out over the span of several days. Requirements also increase during intensified training, such as during a period of intensive trials. However, it is recommended to reduce the intake of carbohydrates when trying to loose weight.

FAT

WHAT IS IT?

All types of fats, in general.

WHERE TO FIND IT?

Different types of fats are found in various animal products, such as: meats, where fat content varies depending on the type of cut; fatty fish, including salmon, tuna, and sardines; egg yolks; dairy products, and butter. Other fat sources include: oils; nuts, including walnuts, hazelnuts, almonds, pistachios peanuts, Brazil nuts, and pecans; seeds; and certain fruits, such as olives and avocados.

WHAT IS ITS ROLE?

Fat has a bad reputation among athletes, but it is essential; fat constitutes part of a cell's membrane and allows for the transport and storage of vitamins. It is also required for the synthesis of essential fat-soluble hormones, such as testosterone, which are needed for building strength.

Moreover, fat is involved in inflammation, healing, and muscle contraction.

For instance, the Omega-3 fatty acids contained in salmon are cardio-protective, improve cognitive function and lower inflammation. On a culinary level, fats are flavor enhancers; they bring a certain smoothness to food, which makes it taste better.

For health and performance, it is preferable to avoid an excess of saturated fatty acids, such as those contained in cheese, butter, deli meats, palm oil, and processed food, and, instead, favor vegetable fats, such as rapeseed, canola, and olive oil.

HOW MUCH DO YOU NEED?

Given the crucial role of fat to the body, it is important to consume at least .45 g of fat per pound of body weight a day, or 1 g per kg a day.
Priority should be given to oils rich in essential fatty acids, such as rapeseed, olive, pumpkin, coconut and walnut oil – which is also high in the antioxidant, vitamin E.
When used for seasoning, a mixture of half canola oil with half olive oil seems an ideal combination for an athlete.
Around 7-10% of daily fat requirements should come from saturated fat, such as a small portion of butter.

REQUIREMENTS CAN VARY

Fat requirements are rarely increased.
Even though fat is an important source of energy for endurance events, there is no need to increase fat intake before a competition. The body's stored fat reserves can provide enough energy to run several marathons, even for very thin individuals. In contrast, it is recommended to reduce your fat intake when seeking to lose weight, since fat is high in calories, containing 9 calories per gram. Fat should never be completely removed from the diet.

BODY FAT

The percentage of body fat is measured using various methods, such as skinfold measurements and biometric scales. The most accurate way to measure body fat is DEXA scanning.

A male professional soccer player should have a fat mass between 7%-12% of his total weight.

Even though body fat can be used as a major energy source, especially during endurance events exceeding 30 minutes, it also constitutes a dead weight that can inhibit performance, and, therefore, must be kept under control.

Fat mass should not go below 6% for men, or 14% for women, since it can increase the risk of injury.

VITAMINS, MINERALS, AND TRACE NUTRIENTS

These nutrients are essential for proper cell function, and the system in general.

1/ VITAMINS

Vitamins are involved in many biological functions, including those relating to enzymes, hormones, and inflammation, as well as the immune system. They also are used in neurotransmission and the release of energy via the metabolism of macronutrients and antioxidants. Vitamin intake must be regular and in sufficient quantities, guaranteed through a balanced diet, **rich in fruit, vegetables, and whole grains.**
For an athlete, vitamin requirements are increased due to strenuous and continued physical activity.
Vitamins are essential for proper muscular function. Antioxidants counteract the increase of free radicals, which are produced in large quantities during exercise. The primary antioxidants are vitamin C, vitamin E, and vitamin A, in the form of beta carotene.

2/ MINERALS

The main minerals are calcium, magnesium, phosphorus, potassium, and sodium.
Calcium is essential for bone building. Calcium must be taken in sufficient doses, in combination with phosphorus and vitamin D, to prevent stress fractures among runners.
Magnesium is also an essential mineral, necessary for proper muscular function and fighting stress. It is either circulating or stored in red blood cells.
Symptoms of magnesium deficiency include cramps, muscle pain, palpitations, and tingling, which all prevent an athlete from achieving peak performance.

3/ TRACE MINERALS

Copper plays an important role in the prevention of oxidative stress and contributes to the proper function of many enzymes.

Iron is an essential nutrient for an athlete. It aids in the transportation and storage of oxygen, boosts energy production, strengthens the immune system, and increases the body's endurance. Activity speeds up iron usage, with significant depletion in the gastrointestinal system during a marathon.

Two of the foods richest in iron are liver and meat, especially beef. Mussels are also particularly high in iron, even more so than meat. Iron is only minimally present in vegetables, and iron of plant origin has a lower bioavailability than that from animal products.

Selenium is also important for an athlete, as it regulates inflammation and immune responses. It plays an essential role in the management of oxidative stress, which is responsible for cellular aging and fatigue.

Selenium is found in protein-rich foods such as meat, poultry, and fish, as well as in whole grains and nuts.

Zinc is essential for an athlete. It is very active in the oxidative process and ensures the proper functioning of a large number of essential enzymes used to synthesize hormones, such as testosterone or insulin, which is vital to an athlete. Zinc is found in beef, white beans, peanuts, and oysters.

BEVERAGES

When discussing sports nutrition, we often focus on food and overlook beverages. Hydration, however, is a very important aspect of athletic performance. Water makes up 60-70% of body mass; muscles contain 73% water and only 15% fat. Water, therefore, plays a fundamental role in all major bodily functions, including all mechanisms linked to performance. The onset of thirst is a late signal; by this point, the body has already long passed the point of dehydration. It is commonly agreed that a water deficit of 2% of body weight – or when thirst occurs – can reduce athletic performance by nearly 20% and increases the risk of injury.

It is important to hydrate regularly throughout the day, with a minimum daily water intake of two to three liters per day, outside training. Having said this, water requirements depend on various factors, including: body weight; intensity, type and duration of activity; and weather conditions. Water intake should be greater during extremely hot weather and when training at high altitudes.

BASIC ADVICE ON HYDRATION AND EXERCISE

- Before working out: Be sure to arrive at training or competition already properly hydrated. This seems trivial, yet field studies carried out on top-level athletes demonstrate that a significant number of athletes begin their exercise already dehydrated, and drinks consumed during activity could not cover the losses. Drinking regularly throughout the day ensures proper hydration. Also, check the color of your urine; clear or very light yellow urine is a good indicator of adequate hydration.

- During exercise: Drink a few sips of water regularly, approximately every 15 minutes. It is recommended to weigh yourself immediately before and after exercise. The weight lost during activity corresponds to the amount of sweat that was not compensated through hydration.

- After working out: To properly rehydrate, it is advisable to lose no more than 2% of body weight during exercise. It is recommended to drink 20-24 ounces of fluid per pound of body weight lost during exercise, which equates to 600-720 ml per .5 kg. Beyond this threshold, dehydration becomes too significant, and will affect both physical and mental performance. To help with recovery, it is recommended to drink alkaline water that is rich in bicarbonate – where bicarbonate is greater than 2,000mg/L.

USEFUL INFORMATION

Swimmers must also take care to hydrate optimally. The mineral water brand, Orezza, is ideal for sports because it is free from nitrates and sodium, yet rich in magnesium and bicarbonates.

Orezza hydrates athletes.
Use Layar to know more
about it (see Page 2)

S.Senaux As Monaco

BEVERAGES	Comments	Daily	Before	During	After
Still or Tap Water	Still water generally contains very little sodium. It can be used throughout the day. During long-term effort or recovery, it may be necessary to add a pinch of salt per liter.	X	X	X	X
Sparkling Mineral Water	Sparkling water can be consumed throughout the day. The presence of gas makes it less advisable for use during exercise. Sparkling water is recommended for rest and recovery, however, especially waters high in sodium and bicarbonate.	X			X
Sports Drinks	Drinks intended for exercise. They usually contain carbohydrates. Depending on the brand, other nutrients may be present, including vitamins, minerals, and amino acids.			X	
Recovery Drinks	Drinks aimed at athletes. These drinks generally contain protein, carbohydrates, and minerals – at a minimum, they will have sodium and potassium. Recovery protein shakes are an example of this type of beverage.				X
Soda	Soda is not recommended for use in sports, due to its high sugar levels and carbonation. It is also not a good recovery drink, as it is low in protein and minerals. Soda is not good for performance or obtaining an ideal body composition. Limit consumption.				
Coffee	Caffeine can enhance performance, but only for those who re-spond well to it. Attention must be taken, as caffeine increases body temperature during exercise, leading to diuresis. The consumption of several cups of coffee prior to exercise in a hot environment is, therefore, not recommended.	X	X		
Milk	Milk is an excellent, natural recovery drink, especially choco-late milk. It rehydrates very well, is great for muscle recovery, and is as effective as a sugary drink in replenishing glycogen stores. It contains vitamin D, calcium, phosphorus, potassium, and magnesium, which all aid in recovery.	X			X
Alcohol	Alcohol is not recommended for athletes. Alcohol negatively interferes with recovery. It also affects rehydration, slows down tissue repair, alters sleep patterns, and promotes bleeding.				

COOKING METHODS

Athletes require a large amount of nutrients, so it is essential to preserve as many vitamins, minerals and antioxidants as possible during the cooking process. Steaming and cooking without added water are the methods that retain the most vitamins and nutrients.

Pan-cooking on the stovetop increases nutrient loss, especially at very high temperatures.

Finally, boiling food and cooking in water could result in a considerable loss of nutrients, particularly vitamin C and B-group vitamins.

There is now superior-quality cookware such as the **Zepter Metal 316L**, whose triple-thick base cooks gently at low temperatures, without requiring added water or oil, resulting in food that is healthier, and retains its natural aromas, flavors, and nutrients.

In general, one must avoid cooking at very high temperatures that can break down fats and food, creating undesirable compounds that are harmful to health.

For the recipes in this book, cooking times are reduced to keep the vegetables crisp and retain the most nutrients.

Olive and coconut oils are ideal for cooking, but it is important to not let the oil smoke or overheat, as it will start to break down. A mixture of olive with rapeseed or nut oil is perfect for seasonings and salad dressings.

To store and re-heat food, use glass receptacles, such as Pyrex, or vacuum containers, like those from VacSy.

Fresh fruits and vegetables lose their nutrients during storage and transportation.

It is best to choose local, seasonal produce and consume it soon after purchase.

USEFUL INFORMATION

Make use of cooking water to recover the nutrients, minerals and water-soluble vitamins that seeped into it. Folate, also known as vitamin B9, is sensitive to light, so store flour, which is rich in folate, in a dark place. Vitamin A is very sensitive to oxygen. For example, if you over-beat your omelet, you will lose half of its vitamin A.

ZEPTER Cookware
Download the Layar app to learn more (see p. 2)

COOKING UTENSILS

In order to prepare the recipes in this book, you will need the following basic equipment.

- Aluminum foil
- Baking dishes and loaf pan
- Baking sheet
- Blender or immersion blender, and an electric mixer
- Colander
- Cooking scale
- Cutting board
- Frying pan, preferably without a non-stick coating, for cooking meat, or high-quality pans, such as Zepter Metal 316L with a triple-thick base, for cooking vegetables and meat
- Grater
- Large saucepan with lid, for pasta
- Mandoline slicer
- Measuring cup
- Non-stick frying pan to warm or sauté vegetables
- Paper towels
- Parchment paper
- Plastic wrap
- Pyrex-style receptacles for food storage
- Salad bowl
- Scissors
- Small kitchen knife
- Small strainer / sieve
- Timer
- Tongs
- Vegetable paring knife
- Vegetable peeler
- Whisk
- Wooden spoon

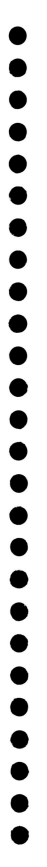
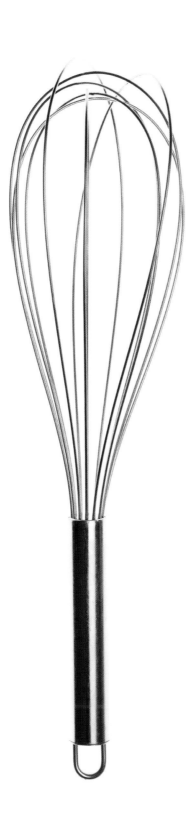

INGREDIENTS

USEFUL INFORMATION

Buy organic and non-GMO produce, whenever possible. Purchase whole grain products, such as whole wheat pasta and brown rice, which are richer in micronutrients.

SPICES

- Black pepper
- Chili powder
- Coriander seeds
- Fennel seeds
- Vanilla beans, or extract
- Ground cinnamon
- Ground cumin
- Ground turmeric
- Nutmeg powder
- Salt

CONDIMENTS/BROTH

- Apple cider vinegar
- Balsamic vinegar
- Red wine vinegar
- White balsamic, rice or white wine vinegar
- Olive, rapeseed, canola and/or coconut oil
- French-style mustard
- Chicken broth
- Vegetable broth

STAPLE GOODS

- Agave syrup
- Baking chocolate
- Baking powder
- Brown rice
- Bulgur
- Chickpeas (canned)
- Dates and dried cranberries
- Diced tomatoes (canned)
- Eggs
- Flour
- Garlic
- Ginger
- Goji berries
- Honey
- Kidney beans (canned)
- Lemon
- Lentils
- Nuts (hazelnuts, walnuts, cashew nuts, almonds, peanuts)
- Oats
- Onions
- Parmesan Cheese
- Pasta (penne, corkscrew, lasagna)
- Polenta
- Powdered sugar
- Quinoa
- Ramen, soba, or udon noodles
- Seeds (flax, sesame, pumpkin, pine nuts, chia)
- Sugar
- Sun-dried tomatoes in oil
- Tomato concentrate
- Wheatberries or farro
- White beans (canned)
- Whole-wheat couscous

MEAL PLANNING

BREAKFAST

When a person wakes up, blood sugar is low and the body is dehydrated.

Working out on an empty stomach does not produce the same quality results as when breakfast was eaten beforehand.
It is estimated that breakfast should cover 25-30% of the day's energy intake. It's an important meal!
A balanced breakfast can boost sports results, enhance intellectual performance, improve mood, and regulate body weight.
As research shows, breakfast is a crucial meal when striving for peak performance.

WITHOUT BREAKFAST, ATHLETIC PERFORMANCE DECREASES BETWEEN 5-10%, EVEN IF THE TRAINING TAKES PLACE IN THE EVENING.

HEALTHY SNACKS

It is highly recommended to have a snack in the afternoon.

A snack can be consumed one-to-two hours before exercise, depending on the time of the workout, for both training and competition.
It should be easily digestible and low in fat.
Healthy snacks include: fruit salad; fat-free dairy products, such as 0% yogurt; cereal or granola; apple sauce; one rice cake; and a protein or energy bar.

USEFUL INFORMATION

It is ideal to wait one to two hours between the end of breakfast and the beginning of training.

Breakfast should always include: water; a lean protein, such as eggs, egg whites, turkey, or a low fat dairy product; fruit, and some form of complex carbohydrate, such as cereal, muesli, granola, oatmeal, or whole grain bread.

It is important to include protein at this meal in order to help sustain energy, especially during a period of intense training, before a competition, or during muscle growth and development.

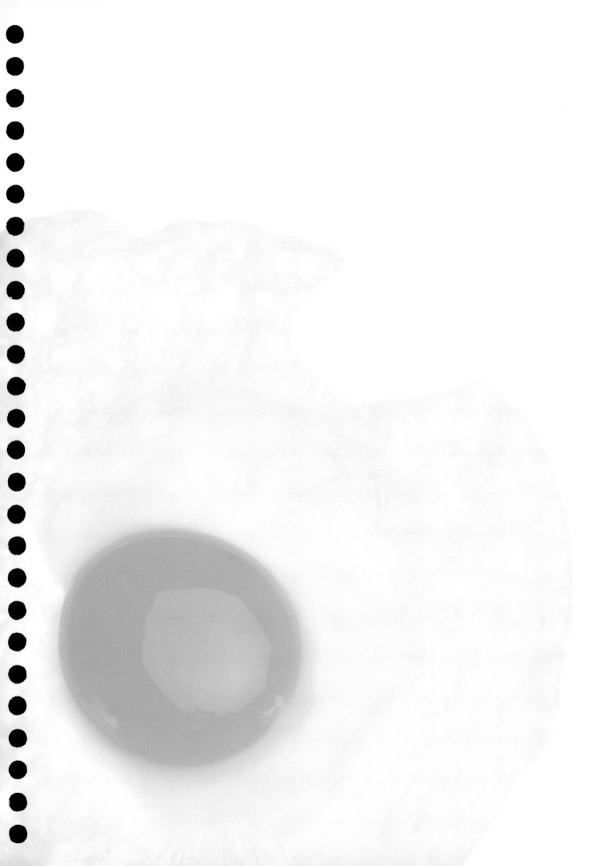

RECIPES FOR DAILY WORKOUTS

Regular, daily training is essential for an athlete, in terms of raising their overall fitness level, as well as building muscle mass.
Bone density can be maintained through an adequate intake of protein, calcium, and vitamin D.
Nutrition for the brain should not be forgotten. Remember to consume carbohydrates with a low glycemic index, along with a variety of fruits, vegetables and fish rich in Omega-3, such as salmon.
The immune system is stimulated by foods high in iron, vitamin C, vitamin E, zinc, and copper.
Berries, olives, walnuts, and hazelnuts are rich in poly-phenols and boost immunity.
It is important to eat a wide variety of foods; choose fruits and vegetables in a wide array of colors to provide an equally wide range of vitamins, minerals, antioxidants, and other nutrients.

WHAT SHOULD LUNCH OR DINNER INCLUDE?

At least one portion of raw vegetables, can be seasoned with salt and pepper, or oil and vinegar.
One portion of fish or meat.
A large serving of vegetables.
One piece of fruit, either fresh or cooked.
One portion of starch, such as grains, potatoes, beans, or lentils. (Portion size should be adjusted to the athlete's individual build and training load.)
One dairy product.
A small quantity of fat, preferably rapeseed, nut, canola, coconut or olive oil.

The meal should last 35 minutes, and include regular hydration.

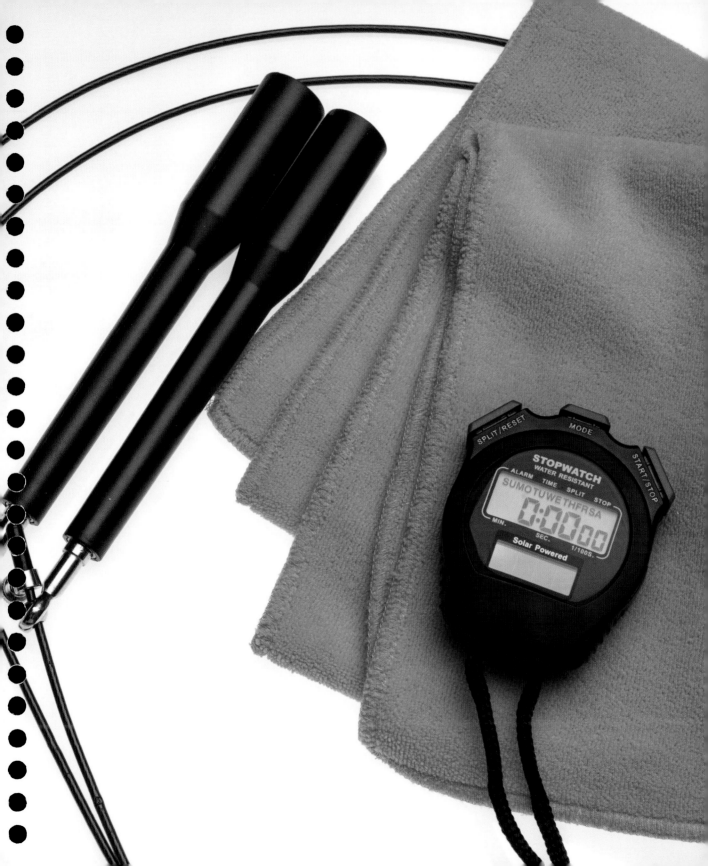

RECIPES FOR COMPETITION

ON EVENT DAY, PRIOR TO EXERCISE, THE GOALS ARE SIMPLE :

Be sufficiently hydrated.
Fuel your body through healthy eating.
Allow time for digestion.
Stabilize blood sugar levels.

Hydration is crucial.
Gastric emptying evacuates only 20-27 fluid ounces per hour, or 600-800 ml. Consuming larger volumes than these increases the risk of stomach upset. The ideal temperature for beverages is between 50-60° F (10-15° C).

Meals should be eaten three-to-four hours prior to competition.
At least three hours should elapse between the end of the meal and the beginning of warm-up exercises. Otherwise, blood flow will be diverted to both the muscles, as well as the digestive system, leading to impaired performance. When competing or training in the evening, it is important that an athlete eats a healthy snack to help properly fuel the body.

The objective is to stabilize blood sugar. Therefore, it is important to avoid competing on an empty stomach, without proper fuel, or in a state of reactive hypoglycemia, which can happen if sugars with a high glycemic index are consumed too soon before a competition.

Limit fat intake. Fats increase digestion time, from anywhere between two to six hours. Foods to avoid include: cheese, fatty meats, fried foods, creamy sauces, pastries, and chocolate. It is better to opt for low-fat cottage cheese or yogurt.

Fruits and vegetables can be consumed, but limit fiber.
To avoid digestive discomfort, tomatoes should be eaten with the skins removed. Carrots should be peeled, and are best served as a purée. Zucchini and eggplant should be peeled and seeded. Only fresh, extra-thin string beans should be chosen. Only eat the asparagus tips, artichoke hearts, and white parts of leeks. Fruits are best eaten skinless or puréed.

Facilitate digestion.
Digestive comfort is paramount when in competition. Systematically eliminate foods known to disrupt the digestive system.
Be wary of heavy sauces and fried foods, as fat slows down digestion.

RECIPES FOR RECOVERY

For all sports, recovery repairs and rebuilds muscles and tissues worn down during physical activity, as well as prepares the body for its next workout and competition. Recovery must begin as soon as possible, even if hunger pangs are not apparent. Nutrient absorption is best immediately following exercise.

Recovery guidelines after exercise are simple.

1/Hydrate
An athlete is typically water deficit after exercise, and therefore must properly rehydrate to compensate for the loss of fluids. An athlete must drink 20-24 oz. of water for each pound of weight lost during competition or training, or 600-720 ml per ½ kilo. Be sure to check your weight before and after exercise.

2/Eat carbohydrates and proteins as soon as possible after exercise. The combination of these two macronutrients is crucial for recovery.

3/Fight against acids, such as lactic acid, that build up during intense exercise. It is recommended to consume foods and beverages with alkalizing properties, including a variety of fruits and vegetables, as well as water that is rich in bicarbonate – where bicarbonate is greater than 2,000mg/L.

HOW TO ADAPT THE RECIPES
TO YOUR INDIVIDUAL BODY TYPE

To customize the recipes for your body weight, please refer to the chart below.
How to change the amount of ingredients to suit your build:

BODY WEIGHT	LESS THAN 130 LB (60 KG)	BETWEEN 130-176 LB (60-80 KG)	BETWEEN 176-198 LB (80-90 KG)	BETWEEN 198-231 LB (90-105 KG)
TARGET PORTION SIZE PER PERSON	Meat & Fish: 4-5 oz. (120-150 g)	Meat & Fish: 5-6 oz. (150-180 g)	Meat & Fish: 6-7 oz. (180-210 g)	Meat & Fish: 7-8 oz. (210-240 g)
RECIPE ADJUSTMENT*	Decrease the quantity of meat or fish by: 2 oz. (60 g) per recipe 1 oz. (30 g) per person	No adjustment necessary: Recipes are designed for a 154 lb (70 KG) person	Increase the quantity of meat or fish by: 2 oz. (60 g) per recipe 1 oz. (30 g) per person	Increase the quantity of meat or fish by: 4 oz. (120 g) per recipe 2 oz. (60 g) per person

BODY WEIGHT	BETWEEN 231-264 LB (105-120 KG)	BETWEEN 264-299 LB (120-136 KG)	HIGHER THAN 299 LB (136 KG)
TARGET PORTION SIZE PER PERSON	Meat & Fish: 8-9 oz. (240-270 g)	Meat & Fish: 9-10 oz. (270-300 g)	Meat & Fish: 10-12 oz. (300-360 g)
RECIPE ADJUSTMENT*	Increase the quantity of meat or fish by: 6 oz. (180 g) per recipe 3 oz. (90 g) per person	Increase the quantity of meat or fish by: 8 oz. (160 g) per recipe 4 oz. (120 g) per person	Double the quantities of the entire recipe

*Recipes serve 2

While meat and fish servings are simple to standardize, the portion size for starch depends on many factors, including build, training load, propensity to gain fat, and whether the athlete is in competition or not. It is, therefore, difficult to determine a standard serving size. We recommend between ¼c. to 1 c., or between 2 oz. (60 g), weight before cooking, for low energy expenditure, to 8 oz. (227 g), for very high energy expenditure, per person, depending on size and activity for foods such as pasta, rice, semolina, bulgur, and quinoa.

Amounts of vitamin C, iron and magnesium:
The values below compare the amounts of vitamin C, iron and magnesium in this book with the Recommended Dietary Allowance (RDA). Men and women have the same RDA for vitamin C. As RDA values for iron and magnesium differ between men and women, an average has been used.

	RDA MEN	RDA WOMEN	VALUE USED IN THIS BOOK
VITAMIN C	110 mg	110 mg	110 mg
IRON	9 mg	16 mg	12.5 mg
MAGNESIUM	420 mg	360 mg	390 mg

RDA: Recommended Dietary Allowance

MEAT

NORMAL TRAINING	WEIGHT LOSS	RECOVERY	PROTEIN 46 g	CARBO-HYDRATES 49 g	FAT 5 g	CALORIES 425 Calories per serving

ASIAN SOUP WITH SOBA NOODLES AND CHICKEN

Setup and preparation: Approx. 30 minutes
Makes 3 ½ c. (8 dl)
Makes 2 servings

INGREDIENTS

- 4 ½ c. (1.2 l) vegetable broth, heated
- 3 tbsp. soy sauce
- 1 stalk of lemon grass, cut into four pieces
- 1 shallot, cut into thin rings
- 1 clove garlic, minced
- 1 carrot, julienned
- 3 ½ oz. (100 g) leeks, sliced into thin rings

- 10 ½ oz. (300 g) chicken breast, cut into 1/4" (1 cm) strips, approx. ⅔ lb.
- 3 ½ oz (100 g) soba noodles

- 1 oz. (30 g) bean sprouts
- A few fresh coriander leaves
- 1 lime, sliced into wedges

PREPARATION

1. Bring the broth, soy sauce and lemon grass to a boil. Add the shallot, garlic, carrot and leeks. Lower heat and simmer for 15 minutes.

2. Add the chicken, and simmer for 5 minutes on very low heat, making sure the water does not boil. Add the noodles. Cook for an additional 5 minutes, or until the noodles are al dente.

3. Serve garnished with bean sprouts, coriander, and lime.

USEFUL INFORMATION

- Substitute basil for the coriander.
- Substitute lean strips of beef for the chicken.
- For extra spice, season with Sriracha or chili powder.

This dish is very low in fat. It is an excellent meal for pre-training or recovery.

MUSCLE MASS BUILDING	PROTEIN 54 g	CARBO-HYDRATES 74 g	FAT 16 g	CALORIES 656 Calories per serving

CHICKEN AND VEGETABLE COUSCOUS

Setup and preparation: Approx. 30 minutes
Makes 2 servings

INGREDIENTS

- 1 c. (2.5 dl) vegetable broth
- 7 oz. (200 g) carrots, halved and quartered
- 2 zucchini, halved and quartered into 1" (2 cm) pieces
- 4 ½ oz. (125 g) medium grain couscous

- 3 ½ oz. (100 g) chickpeas (canned, drained)
- 2 tbsp. fresh mint, chopped
- 1 pinch cinnamon or cayenne pepper
- salt and pepper, to taste

- 1 tbsp. oil for cooking
- 2 garlic cloves, crushed
- 10 ½ oz. (300 g) chicken breast cut into 6 strips, approx. ⅔ lb.
- 1 tsp. salt
- pepper to taste
- 1 ½ oz. (40 g) unsalted pistachios, shelled and coarsely chopped

PREPARATION

1. Bring the broth to a boil in a large saucepan, and add the carrots and zucchini. Lower the heat and simmer, covered, for 10 minutes. Remove from heat, and add the couscous. Cover, until all liquid is fully absorbed, about 5 minutes. Fluff couscous with a fork.

2. Add the chickpeas and mint to the cooked couscous. Season and mix with a fork.

3. Mix the oil and garlic in a bowl. Add the chicken strips, season and mix well. Heat a non-stick frying pan on medium heat. Add the marinated chicken and cook for 5 minutes, making sure to brown the strips on all sides. Remove from heat. Sprinkle the couscous with pistachios, and place the chicken strips on top.

USEFUL INFORMATION

This dish can be enjoyed during periods of intense weight training, as it is rich in proteins, and provides average amounts of carbohydrates and fat. It is recommended to avoid this dish within 48 hours prior to competition, as chickpeas may cause digestive discomfort.

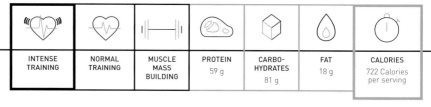

INTENSE TRAINING	NORMAL TRAINING	MUSCLE MASS BUILDING	PROTEIN 59 g	CARBO-HYDRATES 81 g	FAT 18 g	CALORIES 722 Calories per serving

PASTA WITH BROCCOLI, SQUASH AND CHICKEN

Setup and preparation: Approx. 30 minutes
Makes 2 servings

INGREDIENTS

- 1 ½ c. (200 g) short pasta (such as corkscrew), preferably whole wheat
- boiling water, salted
- 1 c. (200 g) broccoli florets
- 1 c. (300 g) squash, such as butternut, diced into ½" (2 cm) cubes
- 1 lb (300 g) chicken breast, cut into ¼" (1 cm) strips

- ¼ c. (40 g) pumpkin seeds

- 1 ½ c. (100 g) baby spinach leaves
- 2 tbsp. nonfat Greek yogurt
- ¼ tsp. nutmeg
- ground pepper

PREPARATION

1. Cook the pasta, broccoli and squash in a pot of salted, boiling water for 7 minutes. Lower heat, add the chicken strips and simmer – making sure the water does not boil – for another 5 minutes, or until the pasta is al dente. Do not drain yet.

2. While the pasta is cooking, roast the pumpkin seeds in a dry, hot frying pan on the stovetop over medium heat until they are golden brown, about 2-3 minutes.

3. Add the baby spinach leaves to the pot with the pasta and chicken. Drain immediately. Add the Greek yogurt, season and mix. Sprinkle with roasted pumpkin seeds.

USEFUL INFORMATION

This dish is very high in protein, with 59 g per portion. It is an ideal meal to help with muscle recovery and growth after weight training and body building.

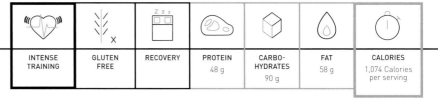

| INTENSE TRAINING | GLUTEN FREE | RECOVERY | PROTEIN 48 g | CARBO-HYDRATES 90 g | FAT 58 g | CALORIES 1,074 Calories per serving |

WARM RICE SALAD WITH TURKEY

Setup and preparation: Approx. 30 minutes
Makes 2 servings

INGREDIENTS

- 1 c. (200 g) brown rice
- boiling water, salted
- 3 ½ oz. (100 g) peas, fresh or frozen
- 1 ear of corn, kernels removed, or ¾ c. (170 g) frozen or canned corn, drained

- 3 tbsp. olive, rapeseed or canola oil
- 4 tbsp. red wine vinegar
- 1 tsp. salt

- 1 orange, divided into wedges, seeds removed
- 1 avocado, chopped
- 10 ½ oz. (300 g) sliced, cooked turkey, approx. ⅔ lb.
- 1 ½ oz. (40 g) pine nuts, roasted in a dry frying pan until golden brown

PREPARATION

1. Prepare the rice as directed on the package. 4 minutes before the rice is finished, add the peas and corn kernels, and continue cooking. When finished, drain any excess water off in a colander. Place in a saucepan, and fluff the rice with a fork.

2. For the vinaigrette: mix the oil with the vinegar and salt. Pour over the rice, and mix well.

3. Add all other ingredients to the rice and toss.

USEFUL INFORMATION

Suggestions:
- Substitute strips of grilled chicken breast, diced salmon, or smoked salmon for the turkey.
- Substitute walnut or flaxseed oil for the rapeseed oil.

While high in calories, this dish is a good energy source of healthy fats and whole-grain carbohydrates. It is also a good source of the antioxidant vitamins, A and E. An ideal meal for post-training.

| NORMAL TRAINING | GLUTEN FREE | PROTEIN 43 g | CARBO-HYDRATES 58 g | FAT 15 g | CALORIES 539 Calories per serving |

BRAISED CHICKEN AND SWEET POTATO PURÉE

Setup and preparation: Approx. 30 minutes
Cooking time: Approx. 50 minutes
2 servings

INGREDIENTS

- A small amount of oil for cooking, such as olive oil, use as little as possible
- 1 lb (500 g) skinless chicken pieces, such as thighs cut in half, drumsticks and upper thigh
- 1 tbsp. turmeric powder
- ½ tsp salt
- pepper, to taste

- 1 onion, quartered
- 7 oz. (200 g) celery, chopped approx. ½" (1.2 cm) thick
- 7 oz. (200 g) carrot sticks, approx. 1" (2.5 cm) in length
- 1 ½ c. (4 dl) chicken broth
- 2 tbsp. white Balsamic vinegar (rice or white wine vinegar can be substituted)
- 2 tbsp. flat leaf parsley, coarsely chopped

Sweet potato purée

- ½ tbsp. olive oil
- 1 garlic clove, chopped
- 14 oz. (400 g) sweet potato, diced into 1" (2.50 cm) cubes
- 3 ½ oz. (100 g) starchy white potatoes, diced into 1" (2.5 cm) cubes
- ½ c. (1 dl) vegetable broth
- salt, to taste

PREPARATION

1. Heat the oil in a cast iron pan. Cook the chicken parts on high heat, turning them so they are browned on all sides, about 5 minutes, total. Remove and season with the turmeric, salt and pepper. Place on paper towels to absorb excess cooking oil.

2. Sauté the onion, celery and carrots until soft in the same pan that was used for the chicken parts. Pour in the broth and bring to a boil. Reduce the heat. Add the chicken, stir. Braise, on low heat, covered, for 50 minutes. Add the vinegar and parsley, stir.

3. While the chicken is braising, heat the olive oil in a large saucepan. Sauté the garlic, sweet potatoes and starchy potatoes for 3 minutes, and add the broth. Bring to a boil, then lower heat. Cover and cook, on low heat, for 20 minutes, or until the potatoes are soft. Remove the pan from the heat, but do not drain. Add salt and mash using a potato masher or fork.

USEFUL INFORMATION

This is a well-balanced meal; it has an average amount of protein and carbohydrates, while being moderate in fat. It can be accompanied by crudités or another vegetable starter, as well as a fruit-based dessert. This dish contains turmeric, a spice rich in polyphenols, which have strong antioxidant and anti-inflammatory properties.

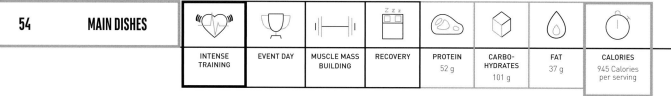

INTENSE TRAINING	EVENT DAY	MUSCLE MASS BUILDING	RECOVERY	PROTEIN 52 g	CARBO-HYDRATES 101 g	FAT 37 g	CALORIES 945 Calories per serving

CHICKEN AND BULGUR SALAD

Setup and preparation: Approx. 30 minutes
Makes 2 servings

INGREDIENTS

- 2 c. (7 dl) vegetable broth
- 7-8 oz. (200 g) bulgur,
approx. 1 c.
- 1 tomato, diced
- 1 cucumber, peeled and diced
- 1 shallot, finely chopped
- ¼ c. (half of one small bunch)
fresh coriander or parsley, finely
chopped

- ½ c. (1 dl) lemon juice
- ¼ c. (½ dl) olive oil
- ½ tsp. salt, some pepper
- 1 ½ oz. (50 g) dried dates, diced

- A sprinkling of pine nuts, roasted in a dry frying pan until golden
brown, to be used as a garnish
- 1 tbsp. olive oil
- 2 chicken breasts,
approx. 5 ½ oz. (150 g) each.
- ½ tsp. salt
- pepper, to taste

PREPARATION

1. Bring the broth to a boil, add the bulgur and cook for 10 minutes, until bulgur is soft. Drain off any excess water in a fine sieve. Add the tomato, cucumber, shallot and parsley or coriander, and stir well.

2. For the dressing: mix the lemon juice, olive oil, salt, and pepper. Pour over the bulgur, stir. Add the dates and pine nuts.

3. Cook the chicken in a small amount of oil for 10 minutes on each side over medium heat. Season, then cut into slices. Serve with the bulgur.

USEFUL INFORMATION

Suggestions :
- Substitute sirloin steak for the chicken.
- Substitute basil for the coriander.
- Substitute rapeseed oil for the olive oil.

This dish is very high in energy. It is rich in both protein and carbohydrates. It can be consumed before a competition or as a recovery meal.

INTENSE TRAINING	MUSCLE MASS BUILDING	RECOVERY	MICRO-NUTRIENTS	PROTEIN 59 g	CARBO-HYDRATES 99 g	FAT 34 g	CALORIES 938 Calories per serving

DUCK BREAST WITH BRUSSELS SPROUTS AND QUINOA

Setup and preparation: Approx. 30 minutes
Baking time: Approx. 25 minutes
Makes 2 servings

INGREDIENTS

- 5 ½ oz. (150 g) quinoa,
approx. ⅔ c.
- 2 c. (5 dl) vegetable broth
- 1 tbsp. olive oil
- 1 green onion, chopped

- 1 lb. (500 g) Brussels sprouts,
outer leaves removed, and cut in
half, depending on size
- 1 tbsp. olive oil
- 2 tbsp. liquid honey
- 1 tbsp. whole grain mustard
- ½ tsp. salt
- 1 tbsp. balsamic vinegar
- 4 tbsp. dried cranberries

- 1 6 oz. (170 g) duck breast, with
crisscrossed incisions on the fat
- ½ tsp. salt
- pepper, to taste

PREPARATION

1. Bring the quinoa and vegetable broth to a boil. Lower the heat, and simmer, uncovered, for 20 minutes, or until the liquid is absorbed. Heat the oil in a non-stick frying pan, and sauté the green onion until soft. Add the quinoa and sauté an additional 4 minutes, while stirring.

2. Preheat the oven to 400° F (200° C). In a bowl, mix the Brussels sprouts, olive oil, honey, mustard and salt. Place evenly on a baking tray lined with parchment paper. Cook for 25 minutes. Remove, and stir in the vinegar and cranberries.

3. Place an ungreased frying pan, preferably without a non-stick surface, over a high flame and heat until the pan is warm. Place the duck breast, skin side down, in the pan and lower the heat to medium. Cook the duck for 8 minutes, Turn and continue cooking for an additional 4 minutes. Season, wrap in aluminum foil and let stand for 10 minutes, then cut into thin slices. Serve with the quinoa and Brussels sprouts.

USEFUL INFORMATION

This dish is rich in protein and carbohydrates. It also contains a very significant quantity of micronutrients, such as B vitamins, vitamin C, iron, and selenium. Additionally, the Brussels sprouts are rich in polyphenols, plant substances with antioxidant properties, which are very important for athletes.

WEIGHT LOSS	**PROTEIN** 41 g	**CARBO-HYDRATES** 14 g	**FAT** 10 g	**CALORIES** 310 Calories per serving

TURKEY CUTLETS WITH ROASTED WINTER SQUASH

Set up and preparation: Approx. 30 minutes
Baking time: Approx. 20 minutes
Makes 2 servings

INGREDIENTS

- 1 tbsp. oil
- 2 cloves garlic, pressed
- 1 tsp. crushed red pepper flakes
- 1 tbsp. soy sauce,
- 2 lbs. (1 kg) winter squash, such as butternut, peeled, seeded, halved and cut in slices. Weight after preparation: approx. 1 ½ lb. (700 g)

- 1 tbsp. oil
- 2 tbsp. teriyaki sauce
- ½" (2 cm) piece fresh ginger, finely grated
- 10 ½ oz. (300 g) turkey cutlets, approx. ⅔ lb.
- 4 tbsp. fat-free Greek yogurt
- a few sprigs of fresh thyme

PREPARATION

1. Preheat the oven to 430° F (220° C). Mix the oil with the garlic, red pepper flakes and soy sauce. Coat the squash slices with the soy sauce mixture and place on a baking tray lined with parchment paper. Broil in the oven for 20 minutes, until the squash is crispy but not burned.

2. Mix the oil, teriyaki sauce, and ginger. Using a brush, coat the turkey cutlets with the teriyaki mix. Heat a frying pan, and brown the cutlets on medium heat for 3 minutes on each side. Serve with Greek yogurt on the side. Garnish with thyme.

USEFUL INFORMATION

This is a light dish, rich in protein, but fairly low in calories, making it great for leaning out and losing weight.

NORMAL TRAINING	EVENT DAY	RECOVERY	PROTEIN 45 g	CARBO-HYDRATES 93 g	FAT 21 g	CALORIES 741 Calories per serving

CHICKEN STEW WITH FENNEL, ASPARAGUS AND POLENTA

Set up and preparation: Approx. 30 minutes
Cooking time: Approx. 50 minutes
Makes 2 servings

INGREDIENTS

- A small amount of oil for cooking, use as little as possible
- 1 lb. (450 g) skinless chicken parts

- 1 tsp. coriander seeds
- 1 tsp. fennel seeds
- 1 tsp. coarse sea salt
- 2-3 black peppercorns
- 1 ½ c. (3 dl) vegetable broth

- 10 ½ oz. (300 g) fennel bulb, quartered, approx. ⅔ c.
- 8 oz. (200 g) green asparagus, the bottom third peeled, and each stalk cut into two pieces
- 3 oz. (100 g) peas, fresh or frozen

- 7-8 oz. (200 g) medium grain cornmeal (polenta), approx. 1 c.
- 1 ½ c. (4 dl) vegetable broth, boiling

Ingredients with possible traces of gluten
x Vegetable broth

PREPARATION

1. Heat the oil in a large pan. Cook the chicken parts over medium heat, turning them so they are browned on all sides, about 5 minutes, total.

2. Place the spices in grinder, or crush using a mortar and pestle. Add to the chicken, cook briefly. Pour in the broth and bring to a boil. Reduce heat, cover, and simmer for 30 minutes.

3. Add the fennel and asparagus. Simmer, covered, for an additional 15 minutes. Add the peas, and cook for 5 minutes. Remove from heat.

4. Cook the cornmeal in the boiling broth, according to the instructions on the package, stirring constantly. Serve with the chicken stew.

USEFUL INFORMATION

Suggestion:
- Substitute rabbit for the chicken.

This is a well-balanced dish. It contains a substantial amount of protein (45 g per portion) and carbohydrates (93 g per portion). As chicken is a lean meat, this meal is naturally low in fat. It is important to note that corn meal is gluten free, making this dish suitable for people following a gluten-free diet.

NORMAL TRAINING	WEIGHT LOSS	PROTEIN 37 g	CARBO-HYDRATES 12 g	FAT 19 g	CALORIES 338 Calories per serving

VEGETABLE AND BEEF SALAD

Setup and preparation: Approx. 30 minutes
Makes 2 servings

INGREDIENTS

- boiling water, salted
- 5 ½ oz. (150 g) broccoli florets
- 5 ½ oz. (150 g) cauliflower florets
- 5 ½ oz. (150 g) baby carrots, quartered lengthwise

- 3 tbsp. white balsamic vinegar (rice or white wine vinegar can be substituted)
- ½ c. (1 dl) vegetable broth
- 1 tbsp. olive oil
- 1 shallot, finely chopped
- ½ tsp. salt
- pepper, to taste

- A small amount of oil for cooking, use as little as possible
- 2 lean beef steaks, approx. 5 ½ oz. (150 g) each
- ½ tsp. sea salt

Ingredients with possible traces of gluten
x Vegetable broth

PREPARATION

1. Cook the broccoli, cauliflower, and carrots in boiling, salted water for 10 minutes, until soft yet firm, or steam.

2. For the dressing: mix the vinegar with the broth and oil. Add the shallot, salt, and pepper. Pour this mixture over the vegetables, stir, and allow to marinate for 30 minutes.

3. Heat the oil in a frying pan. Sear the steaks for approx. 3 minutes per side, then season with salt. Cut the meat into strips, and serve with the vegetables.

USEFUL INFORMATION

Suggestion:
- Sprinkle the salad with unsalted roasted almonds and/or finely chopped herbs.

This dish is low in calories, and particularly low in carbohydrates. It can be enjoyed as part of a weight-loss diet or during a rest day, when energy demand is low. For a normal training day, it is recommended to add a serving of carbohydrates, or a side dish such as rice, potatoes, quinoa or whole-wheat bread, and/or a carbohydrate-rich dessert, such as compote, fruit salad or rice pudding.

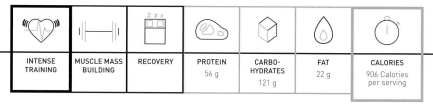

INTENSE TRAINING	MUSCLE MASS BUILDING	RECOVERY	PROTEIN 56 g	CARBO-HYDRATES 121 g	FAT 22 g	CALORIES 906 Calories per serving

VEGETABLE AND BEEF LASAGNA

Setup and preparation: Approx. 30 minutes
Baking time : Approx. 25 minutes
1 one-quart (one-liter) baking dish, lightly oiled
Makes 2 servings

INGREDIENTS

- 1 tbsp. oil
- 10 ½ oz. (300 g) lean ground beef, approx. ⅔ lb.
- 1 clove garlic, chopped
- 2 zucchini, coarsely chopped
- 1 red pepper, coarsely chopped

- 14 oz. (400 g) organic, ready-made tomato sauce
- salt and pepper, to taste

- 12 dry lasagna sheets
- 2 oz. (60 g) grated Parmesan cheese

PREPARATION

1. Heat the oil in a frying pan. Place the ground beef in the pan, and cook over medium heat, for 5 minutes. Add the garlic, zucchini and pepper, and sauté for an additional 5 minutes while stirring.

2. Pour the tomato sauce, salt, and pepper into the beef mixture. Bring to a boil, reduce heat, and simmer, covered, for 15 minutes.

3. Spoon in a small amount of the beef mixture into a baking dish, and spread it out evenly to cover the bottom of the dish. Next, add a layer of overlapping uncooked lasagna sheets, then spoon on a layer of the beef mixture. Continue layering until the beef mixture is used up. Finally, sprinkle the top with Parmesan cheese.

4. Preheat the oven to 390° F (200° C). Bake for 25 minutes in the center rung of the oven.

USEFUL INFORMATION

Ideal with a green salad.
This dish is high in calories, but also carries a significant amount of carbohydrates and protein. It is recommended to be consumed during periods of intensive training.

NORMAL TRAINING	PROTEIN 39 g	CARBO-HYDRATES 59 g	FAT 25 g	CALORIES 617 Calories per serving

SAUTÉED BEEF WITH GREEN ASPARAGUS AND BROWN RICE

Setup and Preparation: Approx. 30 minutes
Makes 2 servings

INGREDIENTS

- ½ c. (125 g) brown rice
- boiling water, salted

- A small amount of oil for cooking, use as little as possible
- 11 oz. (300 g) sirloin steak, cut into ½" (1 cm) strips
- salt and pepper, to taste

- 2 cloves garlic, sliced
- 5 oz. (150 g) green asparagus, the lower third peeled, cut in half lengthwise, then in 1" (2.5 cm) pieces
- 3.5 oz. (100 g) carrots, cut into sticks
- 2 tbsp. lime juice
- 2 tbsp. soy sauce
- 1 tbsp. olive oil
- 2 oz. (60 g) bean sprouts
- 2 green onions, thinly sliced
- 1 oz. (30 g) cashew nuts, coarsely chopped and roasted in a dry frying pan until golden brown

PREPARATION

1. Cook the rice as per the instructions on the package, drain off any excess liquid.

2. Heat the oil in a large wok. Sear meat by portions for 1 minute on high heat. Season, remove from wok.

3. Add a small amount of oil to the wok, if necessary, and sauté the garlic, asparagus, and carrots for 5 minutes on high heat, stirring continuously. Add the lime juice and the remaining ingredients, including the cashews. Stir. Serve with the meat and rice.

USEFUL INFORMATION

Suggestions:
- Garnish with fine herbs or sesame seeds over the rice.
- Substitute sesame or rapeseed oil for the olive oil.

This dish can be enjoyed during normal training or on a rest day.

RECOVERY	EVENT DAY	PROTEIN	CARBO-HYDRATES	FAT	CALORIES
		46 g	89 g	23 g	747 Calories per serving

MEATBALLS IN TOMATO SAUCE

Setup and Preparation: Approx. 30 minutes
Makes 2 servings

INGREDIENTS

- 1 tbsp. olive oil
- 1 onion, cut in half and sliced
- 2 cloves garlic, sliced
- 2 tbsp. tomato concentrate
- 2 cans diced tomatoes, 14 oz. (400 g) each
- 1 tsp. of salt
- pepper to taste
- 4 tbsp. capers, rinsed in cold water

- 10 ½ oz. (300 g) lean ground beef, about ⅔ lb.
- 1 onion, finely chopped
- 1 tsp. ground cumin
- 2 tbsp. finely chopped fresh herbs, such as parsley, mint, etc.
- 1 tsp salt
- pepper, to taste

- A small amount of oil for cooking, use as little as possible

- 8 ½ oz. (240 g) penne pasta, preferably whole wheat
- boiling water, salted

PREPARATION

1. Heat the oil in a saucepan, and sauté the onion and garlic until soft. Add the tomato concentrate, and stir until smooth. Add the tomatoes, salt, and pepper. Simmer, covered on low heat for 20 minutes, or until the sauce has reduced. Remove from heat. Stir in the capers.

2. Using moistened hands to prevent the beef from sticking, mix the ground meat, onion, cumin, herbs, salt and pepper. Knead well until all ingredients are mixed consistently and form a compact mass. Shape into 1 ½" (4 cm) balls.

3. Heat the oil in a frying pan. Cook the meatballs on medium heat, turning them so they are browned on all sides, about 5 minutes, total.

4. Cook the penne in boiling, salted water until al dente. Drain. Top with the tomato sauce and meatballs.

USEFUL INFORMATION

This dish is rich in carbohydrates. It can be enjoyed pre-exercise, as well as during post-activity recovery. Capers are very high in quercetin, a polyphenol substance that is beneficial to an athlete's immune system.

NORMAL TRAINING	GLUTEN FREE	EVENT DAY	RECOVERY	PROTEIN 46 g	CARBO-HYDRATES 86 g	FAT 13 g	CALORIES 645 Calories per serving

BAKED SWEET POTATOES STUFFED WITH LEAN GROUND BEEF

Setup and preparation: Approx. 30 minutes
Baking time: Approx. 50 minutes
Makes 2 servings

INGREDIENTS

- 2 lb. (1 kg) sweet potatoes, cut in two, depending on size
- parchment paper or aluminum foil

- A small amount of oil for cooking, use as little as possible
- 11 oz. (300 g) lean ground beef, approx. ⅔ lb
- ½ tsp. salt
- pepper, to taste

- 1 c. (200 g) fat free cottage cheese
- ¼ c. (50 g) baby spinach or arugula or watercress

PREPARATION

1. Preheat the oven to 400° F (200° C). Wrap the sweet potatoes in parchment paper and bake in the oven for 50 minutes, or until soft.

2. Heat the oil in a pan. Cook the meat for 4 minutes over medium-high heat, season, and remove from the pan.

3. Slit the sweet potatoes lengthwise, and slightly open them. Stuff with the meat, cottage cheese and spinach.

USEFUL INFORMATION

Suggestion :
- You can also prick the potatoes with a fork, and place in the microwave. Cook for approx. 6 minutes.

This meal is low in fat and provides approximatively 90 g – or 6 servings – of carbohydrates per portion. Pair this dish with a salad and a fruit-based dessert.

NORMAL TRAINING	WEIGHT LOSS	MICRO-NUTRIENTS	PROTEIN 42 g	CARBO-HYDRATES 37 g	FAT 14 g	CALORIES 442 Calories per serving

CHILI CON CARNE

Setup and preparation: Approx. 20 minutes
Cooking time: Approx. 40 minutes
Makes 2 servings

INGREDIENTS

- 1 tbsp. cooking oil
- 10 ½ oz. (300 g) lean ground beef, approx. ⅔ lb.
- 1 tsp. salt
- pepper, to taste
- 2 onions, halved and sliced
- 1 clove garlic, sliced
- 1 carrot, cut into slices

- 2 tbsp. tomato concentrate
- 1 c. (2 dl) vegetable broth
- 1 can of peeled, diced tomatoes, 14 oz. (400 g)
- ½ lb. (200 g) green beans, cut in half
- 1 ear of corn, cut into four rounds

- 1 can kidney beans, 5 ½ oz. (150 g), drained and rinsed in cold water
- 1 pinch of chili powder
- 1 tbsp. soy sauce
- some chopped parsley or fresh coriander, as a garnish

PREPARATION

1. Heat the oil in a cast iron skillet. Cook the ground meat for 4 minutes on medium-high heat, while stirring. Add salt and pepper, stir. Add the onion, garlic, and carrot, and sauté for a few minutes.

2. Add the tomato concentrate, and stir until smooth. Add the broth and tomatoes, cover and simmer for 20 minutes. Add the green beans and corn, and simmer an additional 20 minutes.

3. Add the kidney beans, stir, and continue cooking for 10 minutes. Season to taste. Garnish with chopped parsley or coriander.

USEFUL INFORMATION

Suggestions :
- Add 3 ½ oz. (100 g) sliced button mushrooms and bell pepper, when you add the onions, garlic, and carrots.
- Substitute ½ c. (170 g) canned or frozen corn for the ear of corn.

Ideal with bread or potatoes.
This dish is a good source of micronutrients, including iron, zinc, and B vitamins. It is also low in calories and can be enjoyed as part of a weight-loss diet.

WEIGHT LOSS	PROTEIN 54 g	CARBO-HYDRATES 23 g	FAT 18 g	CALORIES 470 Calories per serving

STUFFED VEAL CUTLETS WITH CARROT PURÉE

Setup and preparation: Approx. 30 minutes
Makes 2 servings

INGREDIENTS

- 1 ¼ c. (3 dl) vegetable broth
- 14 oz. (400 g) carrots, peeled, and roughly chopped

- 14 oz. (400 g) cauliflower florets
- 1 tbsp. olive oil
- ½ tsp. salt
- Red pepper flakes or chili powder, to taste

- 2 veal cutlets, 5 oz. (150 g) each, pounded flat with a meat mallet or by the butcher, cut in two, if necessary
- ½ tsp. salt
- pepper, to taste
- 1 ½ oz. (50 g) fresh goat cheese
- 4 sun-dried tomatoes in oil, well drained, cut into strips
- 1 ½ oz. (50 g) celery, cut into small matchsticks
- toothpicks

- A small amount of oil for cooking, use as little as possible

- fresh parsley, coriander or chervil, to use as a garnish

PREPARATION

1. Bring the vegetable broth to a boil. Add carrots, cover, and cook for 25 minutes. Remove from heat. Do not drain.

2. Preheat the oven to 390°F (200° C). While the carrots are cooking, mix the cauliflower with the oil and spices. Spread on a baking tray lined with parchment paper and cook for 30 minutes, until the cauliflower starts to brown and can be pierced with a fork.

3. Season the veal cutlets with salt and pepper. Cover each with half of the fresh goat cheese. Top the cheese with the sun-dried tomatoes and celery sticks, and wrap into a roll, securing with a toothpick.

4. Heat the oil in a frying pan, and cook the veal for 4 minutes on each side.

5. Purée the carrots in a blender or with an immersion blender. Garnish with parsley, coriander or chervil to taste.

USEFUL INFORMATION

This recipe is low in calories and high in protein. It is a perfect light dish to help with weight loss.

Ingredients with possible
traces of gluten
x Vegetable broth

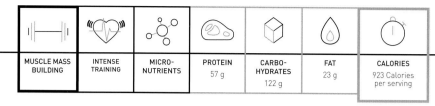

			PROTEIN	CARBO-HYDRATES	FAT	CALORIES
MUSCLE MASS BUILDING	INTENSE TRAINING	MICRO-NUTRIENTS	57 g	122 g	23 g	923 Calories per serving

CHOPPED VEAL WITH PASTA, KALE AND GOAT CHEESE

Setup and preparation: Approx. 30 minutes
Makes 2 servings

INGREDIENTS

- A small amount of oil for cooking, use as little as possible
- 10 ½ oz. (300 g) veal, cut into thin strips, approx. ⅔ lb.
- ½ tsp. salt,
- pepper, to taste

- 1 onion, finely chopped
- 10 ½ oz. (300 g) kale, finely chopped
- 7 oz. (200 g) button mushrooms, sliced
- 2 tbsp. lemon juice
- salt and pepper, to taste

- 1 ¼ c. (300 g) short pasta, such as penne, whole wheat or gluten free
- boiling water, salted

- 3 ½ oz. (100 g) fresh goat cheese, approx. ½ c.
- a few sprigs of fresh thyme

PREPARATION

1. Heat the oil in a frying pan. Add the strips of veal, and cook for 2 minutes, stirring to evenly brown. Season with salt and pepper, and remove from the pan.

2. Using the same pan that the veal was cooked in, sauté the onions, kale and mushrooms for 7 minutes, until soft. Add the lemon juice, salt and pepper. Leave the vegetables to cook, covered, for 5 minutes.

3. Cook the pasta in salted, boiling water until al dente. Drain, and mix with the meat, vegetables and fresh goat cheese. Serve immediately with the thyme.

USEFUL INFORMATION

This is a very complete dish. It contains meat protein, starch, vegetables and a dairy product. Since protein and carbohydrates are quite high, it can be eaten as a single-dish meal. However, adding a raw vegetable starter and/or a fruit dessert can give you an extra nutrient boost. This dish's high carbohydrate and protein content – one portion covers 50-75% of daily protein intake for an athlete weighing 132 lb (60 kilos) – make it ideal for periods of intense muscle use, such as during muscle mass training or intensive training.

MICRO-NUTRIENTS	PROTEIN 46 g	CARBO-HYDRATES 65 g	FAT 44 g	CALORIES 840 Calories per serving

LENTIL SALAD WITH VEAL

Setup and preparation: Approx. 45 minutes
Makes 2 servings

INGREDIENTS

- 5 ½ oz. (150 g) dry lentils

- 1 pink grapefruit, peeled and diced, make sure to reserve any juice that is lost while chopping
- 1 tbsp. white balsamic vinegar (rice or white wine vinegar can be substituted)
- 1 tsp. whole grain mustard
- 3 tbsp. olive oil
- salt and pepper, to taste
- 1 green onion, diced

- 10 ½ oz. (300 g) veal or veal liver, cut into ½" (1 cm) strips
- 2 tsp. Worcestershire sauce
- sea salt, to taste
- pepper from a mill, to taste

- 1 pomegranate, seeded
- ½ c. (one small bunch) fresh tarragon or flat-leaf parsley, coarsely chopped
- 1 ½ oz. (40 g) chopped walnuts, roasted in a dry frying pan

PREPARATION

1. Place the lentils in a saucepan with a liter of cold water. Bring to a boil. Reduce to low heat, and cook for 30 minutes, until the lentils are soft, yet firm. Drain.

2. For the vinaigrette: mix the grapefruit juice with the balsamic vinegar, mustard and oil. Season with salt and pepper. Toss the lentils, with the dressing, onion and diced grapefruit.

3. Heat the oil in a frying pan, and sauté the veal or veal liver for 4 minutes on medium heat, turning over once midway. Add the Worcestershire sauce, stir, and season with salt and pepper.

4. Mix the lentil salad with the pomegranate seeds and tarragon, place the veal or liver on top and sprinkle with nuts.

USEFUL INFORMATION

This dish is very rich in iron. It is ideal for rest and recovery, accompanied by a dessert high in vitamin C, such as kiwi or strawberry. Avoid coffee or tea after the meal, to better absorb the meal's iron.

NORMAL TRAINING	RECOVERY	PROTEIN 45 g	CARBO-HYDRATES 88 g	FAT 47 g	CALORIES 955 Calories per serving

VEAL CUTLETS WITH LEMON, RISOTTO AND FENNEL SALAD

Setup and preparation: Approx. 45 minutes
Makes 2 servings

INGREDIENTS

- 1 tbsp. olive oil
- 1 onion, finely chopped
- 1 c. (200 g) arborio rice
- 1 tbsp. white balsamic vinegar (rice or white wine vinegar can be substituted)
- 2 ½ c. (6 dl) vegetable broth, boiling

- 2 tbsp. olive oil
- 1 organic lemon, juiced
- 6 fresh mint leaves, chopped
- salt and pepper, to taste
- 2 fennel, cut into thin slices using a mandoline

- ½ tbsp. olive oil
- 2 veal cutlets, 5 ½ oz. (150 g) each, approx. ⅔ lb., cut in half
- 1 organic lemon, juiced
- salt and pepper, to taste

- 1 oz. (30 g) grated Parmesan cheese
- salt and pepper, to taste
- ½ oz. (20 g) pine nuts, roasted in a dry frying pan until golden brown

PREPARATION

1. Heat the oil in a saucepan. Sauté the onion until soft, and add the rice. Stir constantly until the rice becomes translucent. Add the vinegar, stir. Gradually pour in the broth by ladleful, stirring often, so that the rice is always covered with liquid. Cook slowly over low-to-medium heat for 20 minutes, until the rice is creamy and al dente.

2. While the risotto is cooking, mix the olive oil, lemon juice, mint, salt and pepper. Pour on the fennel, and toss.

3. Heat the oil in a frying pan, preferably without a non-stick coating. Place the veal cutlets in the pan, and sear for 1 minute on each side. Sprinkle with lemon juice and season with salt and pepper.

4. Add the Parmesan cheese to the risotto, season with salt and pepper, and stir. Sprinkle pine nuts over the fennel salad. Serve the risotto with the veal cutlets and fennel salad.

USEFUL INFORMATION

This is a high energy dish that is best consumed during periods of intensive training, preferably the evening before a sporting event.

NORMAL TRAINING	WEIGHT LOSS	PROTEIN 45 g	CARBO-HYDRATES 15 g	FAT 23 g	CALORIES 447 Calories per serving

PORK TENDERLOIN WITH PEPPERED TOFU

Setup and preparation: Approx. 30 minutes
Makes 2 servings

INGREDIENTS

- 5 ½ oz. (150 g) firm tofu, finely crumbled by hand
- 1 tbsp. Szechuan pepper, crushed
- ½ tsp. salt
- 1 garlic clove, finely chopped
- ½" (2 cm) fresh ginger, grated
- ½ tbsp. olive oil

- 1 tbsp. olive oil
- 2 pork tenderloins, 5 ½ oz. (150 g) each, approx. ⅔ lb total
- ½ tsp. salt

- ½ tbsp. olive oil
- 1 garlic clove, minced
- 1 lb. (400 g) Chinese cabbage, cut into strips, or bok choy, quartered
- 1 tbsp. soy sauce
- 1 tsp. chili powder

Ingredients with possible traces of gluten
x   Soy sauce

PREPARATION

1. Mix the tofu with the Szechuan pepper, salt, garlic, ginger and oil. Cook in a frying pan until golden. Remove from the pan, and set aside.

2. Heat the oil in the same skillet used for the tofu. Cook the tenderloins on medium heat for 4 minutes on each side. Season with salt. Remove from heat and place on a plate. Sprinkle with the tofu mixture and place in an oven at very low heat, to keep warm.

3. For the vegetables, heat the oil in the same skillet. Cook the garlic and vegetables until soft. Add the soy sauce, and simmer, covered, for 5 minutes. Season with chili powder.

USEFUL INFORMATION

Ideal with brown rice, prepared according to the instructions on the package, and sprinkled with coarsely chopped cashew nuts.

This dish is high in protein and low in carbohydrates. It is an ideal dinner when trying to lose weight. At other times, it can be paired with a carbohydrate-rich food, such as a whole grain.

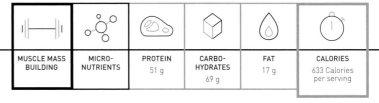

| MUSCLE MASS BUILDING | MICRO-NUTRIENTS | PROTEIN 51 g | CARBO-HYDRATES 69 g | FAT 17 g | CALORIES 633 Calories per serving |

PORK TENDERLOIN
WITH QUINOA AND VEGETABLES

Setup and preparation: Approx. 35 minutes
Makes 2 servings

INGREDIENTS

- 1" (2 cm) piece of fresh ginger, finely grated
- 1 garlic clove, minced
- 2 tbsp. soy sauce
- 10 ½ oz. (300 g) pork tenderloin (also know as pork filet mignon), approx. ⅔ lb.

- 2 ½ c. (6 dl) vegetable broth
- 2 ½ c. (200 g) black or white quinoa
- 7 oz. (200 g) zucchini, cut into ½" wide slices
- 10 ½ oz. (300 g) winter squash, such as butternut, diced into ½" pieces
- 1 tbsp. soy sauce
- 1 tbsp. lemon or lime juice

- A small amount of oil for cooking, use as little as possible
- fresh coriander, as a garnish

PREPARATION

1. Mix the ginger, garlic and soy sauce. Marinate the meat in the soy mixture for 30 minutes, covered.

2. Bring the broth to a boil. Add the quinoa. Cover and simmer on low heat for 5 minutes. Add the vegetables, and simmer for 7 minutes, until the liquid is absorbed; the lid can be removed, if necessary. Season with soy sauce and lemon juice.

3. Heat the oil in a frying pan. Cook the pork tenderloin 4 minutes on each side, and place on top of the quinoa. Sprinkle with coriander.

USEFUL INFORMATION

Suggestion:
- Substitute broccoli or cauliflower for the squash and zucchini.

This dish is rich in protein and contains an average amount of carbohydrate. It also contains significant amounts of micronutrients, including the B vitamins, magnesium, and iron.

FISH AND SEAFOOD

NORMAL TRAINING	MUSCLE MASS BUILDING	WEIGHT LOSS	MICRO-NUTRIENTS	PROTEIN 50 g	CARBO-HYDRATES 29 g	FAT 26 g	CALORIES 550 Calories per serving

ATHLETE'S NIÇOISE SALAD

Setup and preparation: Approx. 30 minutes
Makes 2 servings

INGREDIENTS

- 2 waxy, medium-sized potatoes
- ½ gallon (1 liter) boiling water
- 2 eggs

- 2 artichoke hearts, frozen or canned, thawed or drained, diced
- 1 head of romaine lettuce, washed, dried, and chopped
- 1 ripe tomato, diced
- ½ cucumber, peeled, seeded, and diced
- 2 celery stalks, thinly sliced
- 1 red onion or 2 green onions, sliced into thin rings (red onion) or diced (spring onion)
- ½ red pepper, sliced into strips
- 10 red radishes, sliced
- 3 ½ oz. (100 g) baby fava beans or peas, fresh or frozen

- 2 tbsp. olive oil
- 1 organic lemon, juiced, reserve one 1 tbsp. of juice separately
- 2 tbsp. chicken broth
- salt and pepper, to taste

- 1 tbsp. olive oil
- 2 fresh albacore tuna steaks, 5 ½ oz. (150 g) each
- a pinch of sea salt
- freshly ground black pepper from a pepper mill, to taste
- ½ c. (one small bunch) fresh basil leaves

PREPARATION

1. Place the potatoes, with the skins still on, into a pot of boiling water and cook for 10 minutes. Add the eggs and continue cooking for another 10 minutes. The potatoes are cooked when they offer no resistance when pierced with a sharp knife. Drain, and allow to cool. Peel the potatoes and cut into quarters or eighths, depending on their size. Peel the eggs. Cut into halves and set aside.

2. Gently mix the potatoes, artichoke hearts, lettuce, tomato, cucumber, celery, onion, red pepper, radishes, and fava beans or peas in a large salad bowl.

3. For the dressing: mix the olive oil, lemon juice and chicken broth in a separate bowl, and season to taste. Pour the dressing onto the mixed salad and gently toss.

4. Heat the oil in a non-stick pan, and quickly sear the tuna steaks 1 minute on each side. Season to taste. Dice the tuna into 1" (2 cm) cubes, and baste with the remaining 1 tbsp. lemon juice. Place the halved eggs and diced tuna on top of the salad, and garnish with basil leaves.

USEFUL INFORMATION

Suggestion:
- Omit the potatoes and use whole-wheat bread as an accompaniment.

This salad is a good, lean source of protein (50 g per portion). Therefore, it is recommended to be eaten when building lean muscle.

Ingredients with possible traces of gluten
x Chicken broth

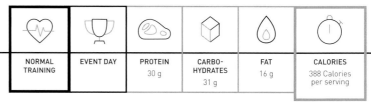

| NORMAL TRAINING | EVENT DAY | PROTEIN 30 g | CARBO-HYDRATES 31 g | FAT 16 g | CALORIES 388 Calories per serving |

GINGER AND ORANGE CARROT SOUP WITH SCALLOPS

Setup and preparation: Approx. 30 minutes
Makes 2 servings

INGREDIENTS

- 1 tbsp. oil
- 1 shallot, finely chopped
- 1" (2 cm) piece of fresh ginger, grated
- 1 lb. (500 g) carrots, peeled and chopped

- 3 c. (7 dl) vegetable broth
- ½ c. (1 dl) orange juice
- salt and pepper, according to taste

- 1 tbsp. oil for cooking
- 10 ½ oz. (300 g) scallops, approx. ⅔ lb.
- salt and pepper, to taste

- 2 tbsp. fat-free Greek yogurt

 Ingredients with possible traces of gluten
x Vegetable broth

PREPARATION

1. Heat the oil in a large saucepan, sauté the shallot and ginger until soft. Add the carrots, and sauté.

2. Pour the broth into the carrot mixture, and simmer, covered, for 20 minutes. Blend into a soup, using an immersion blender. Add the orange juice, salt and pepper. Stir.

3. Heat the oil in a frying pan, and brown the scallops 3 minutes on each side. Season with salt and pepper. Serve the soup topped with scallops and yogurt.

USEFUL INFORMATION

This recipe is to be used as a starter or as a light main course. If consumed as a main dish, accompany it with a healthy carbohydrate-based appetizer and/or dessert, such as compote, fruit salad or rice pudding.

MICRO-NUTRIENTS	PROTEIN 46 g	CARBO-HYDRATES 28 g	FAT 42 g	CALORIES 674 Calories per serving

SALMON CAESAR SALAD WITH KALE

Setup and preparation: Approx. 15 minutes
Makes 2 servings

INGREDIENTS

- 1 tsp. mustard
- 1 tsp. salt
- pepper, to taste
- 3 tbsp. rapeseed or olive oil
- 2 tbsp. white balsamic vinegar (rice or white wine vinegar can be substituted)

- 5 ½ oz. (150 g) kale, finely chopped
- 2 fresh green onions, cut into rings

- 3 slices whole grain bread, diced

- 11 oz. (200 g) organic smoked salmon, cut into strips, approx. ⅔ lb
- 2 hard-boiled eggs, cut in half
- 1 organic lemon, quartered

PREPARATION

1. Warm the the mustard, salt, pepper, and vinegar in a small saucepan. Stir until blended.

2. Put the chopped kale in a large bowl. Pour the dressing over the kale, toss, and let sit for 10 minutes. Add the onions.

3. Preheat the oven to 480° F (250° C). Toast the diced bread on a baking tray placed in the middle rung of the oven for 3 minutes, or in an ungreased frying pan for 5 minutes, stirring the entire time.

4. Divide the marinated kale onto two plates. Sprinkle with the croutons, and surround with the eggs. Top with the salmon strips, garnish with the lemon quarters.

USEFUL INFORMATION

Suggestion :
- Substitute baby spinach or Swiss chard for the kale.

This dish is rich in B vitamins, vitamin E, and omega-3, which have antioxidant and anti-inflammatory properties. This dish is also rich in healthy fat.

MICRO-NUTRIENTS	PROTEIN 39 g	CARBO-HYDRATES 52 g	FAT 17 g	CALORIES 517 Calories per serving

RED POTATO SALAD WITH CALAMARI

Setup and preparation: Approx. 30 minutes
Marinating: Approx. 20 minutes
Makes 2 servings

INGREDIENTS

- 20 oz. (600 g) cooked, small, red-skinned potatoes, quartered, approx. 1 ¼ lb
- 1 shallot, thinly sliced into rings
- ⅔ c. (1.5 dl) vegetable broth, boiling

- 1 tsp. whole grain mustard
- 2 tbsp. white balsamic vinegar (rice or white wine vinegar can be substituted)
- 1 tbsp. rapeseed or olive oil
- salt and pepper, to taste

- A small amount of oil for cooking, use as little as possible
- 1 lb (400 g) calamari, ready to cook, rinsed
- ½ tsp. salt
- pepper, to taste

- 2 heads of little gem lettuce, chopped (romaine can be substituted)
- 1 lemon, quartered

PREPARATION

1. Pour the broth over the cooked, quartered potatoes and shallots. Allow to marinate for 20 minutes. Do not drain.

2. Mix the mustard, vinegar, oil, salt, and pepper. Toss with the marinated potatoes.

3. Heat the oil in a frying pan. Cook the calamari on high heat for 2 minutes, stirring to cook all sides. Season with salt and pepper, and add to the salad. Gently toss.

4. Serve the potato salad on top of a bed of chopped little gem lettuce, and garnish with lemon quarters.
.

USEFUL INFORMATION

Suggestion:
- Replace the calamari with 1 lb (400 g) diced salmon, cut into ½" (2 cm) cubes.

This dish contains average portions of protein, fat, and carbohydrates. It can be eaten on a normal training day. Calamari contains a significant amount of DHA, an Omega-3 fatty acid with anti-inflammatory properties.

NORMAL TRAINING	EVENT DAY	PROTEIN 37 g	CARBO-HYDRATES 32 g	FAT 24 g	CALORIES VALUE 492 Calories per serving

BEETROOT SALAD WITH PEARS AND GOJI BERRIES, GRILLED SOLE

Setup and preparation: Approx. 20 minutes
Makes 2 servings

INGREDIENTS

- 1 lemon, juiced
- 2 tbsp. oil, such as rapeseed or olive oil
- ½ tsp. salt
- pepper, to taste

- 1 lb (400 g) red beets, cooked, quartered or sliced (as preferred)
- 2 tbsp. goji berries

- 2 sole fillets, 6 ½ oz. (180 g) each.
- A small amount of oil for cooking, use as little as possible
- ½ tsp. salt
- pepper, to taste

- 1 pear, seeded and quartered
- 1 oz. (30 g) watercress or baby spinach

 Ingredients with possible traces of gluten
  x Goji berries

PREPARATION

1. Mix the lemon juice with the oil, salt, pepper.

2. Mix the beetroot and the goji berries with the vinaigrette. Marinate for 5 minutes.

3. Heat the oil in a frying pan. Brown the fish fillets over medium heat for 4 minutes on each side. Season with salt and pepper.

4. Add the pear and watercress to the beetroot salad, and toss. Serve with the fish.

USEFUL INFORMATION

Suggestions:
- Add lemon quarters to the pan when cooking fish, to use as a garnish.
- Substitute another white fish for the sole fillets.

This dish contains an average amount of protein, but is low in carbohydrates. To increase carbohydrate intake, it can be accompanied by a starch-based starter or a healthy carbohydrate-based dessert, such as applesauce, fruit salad, or rice pudding. Beetroot is important for sports, as it enhances endurance and athletic performance.

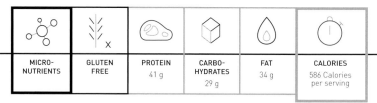

MICRO-NUTRIENTS	GLUTEN FREE	PROTEIN 41 g	CARBO-HYDRATES 29 g	FAT 34 g	CALORIES 586 Calories per serving

WHITE BEAN SALAD
WITH AVOCADO AND SHRIMP

Setup and preparation: Approx. 30 minutes
Makes 2 servings

INGREDIENTS

- 2 tbsp. vinegar
- 3 tbsp. rapeseed or olive oil
- 1 oz. (20 g) arugula
- 1 organic orange, juiced and zest grated
- ½ tsp. salt
- pepper, to taste

- 1 can white beans, 10 ½ oz. (300 g), drained and rinsed
- 1 avocado, diced
- 1 red onion, cut in half and thinly sliced
- 1 grapefruit, divided into wedges or cut in half and sliced

- 1 lb. (400 g) shelled raw shrimp tails (20 normal-sized shrimp)
- A small amount of oil for cooking, use as little as possible
- ½ tsp. of salt
- pepper, to taste
- arugula, used as a garnish

PREPARATION

1. For the dressing, mix the vinegar with the oil, arugula, orange juice and zest, salt, and pepper.

2. Pour the dressing over the beans, and gently toss with the avocado, onion, and grapefruit.

3. Heat the oil in a frying pan, brown the shrimp for 4 minutes on each side. Season with salt and pepper. Serve on top of the salad, and garnish with arugula.

USEFUL INFORMATION

This well-balanced salad is best eaten on a day free from competition, or as part of a post-training meal. Avocado contains healthy fat, and is a good source of vitamin E, which helps decrease inflammation. Both the beans and shrimp provide protein and iron for energy and muscle recovery.

NORMAL TRAINING	PROTEIN 44 g	CARBO-HYDRATES 54 g	FAT 30 g	CALORIES 662 Calories per serving

SALMON WITH MANGO SALSA AND FARRO

Setup and preparation: Approx. 30 minutes
Makes 2 servings

INGREDIENTS

- 1 mango, 10 ½ oz. (300 g), diced
- 1 shallot, minced
- 1 red chili, finely chopped
- 1 tbsp. soy sauce
- 1 tbsp. fresh basil or coriander leaves, finely chopped

- 9 oz. (150 g) wheatberries or farro
- boiling water, salted

- A small amount of oil for cooking, use as little as possible
- 2 portions skinless salmon, 7 oz. (180 g) each
- ½ tsp. salt
- pepper, to taste

- 1 ½ oz. (40 g) arugula, roughly chopped
- 1 pomegranate, seeded
- ¾ oz. (20 g) hazelnuts, coarsely chopped

PREPARATION

1. Mix the mango, shallot, chili, soy sauce and herbs. Set aside.

2. Meanwhile, cook the wheatberries or farro in boiling, salted water, according to instructions on the package.

3. Heat the oil in a pan. Gently brown the salmon for 3 minutes per side. Season with salt and pepper.

4. Drain the farro, and toss with the arugula, pomegranate seeds and hazelnuts. Top with the salmon and mango salsa.

USEFUL INFORMATION

This dish offers a perfect combination of sweet and salty. It also has a good balance of protein, fat, and carbohydrates. It can be eaten during periods of normal training. Salmon is a fatty fish, rich in Omega-3 and vitamin D.

WEIGHT LOSS	GLUTEN FREE	PROTEIN 37 g	CARBO-HYDRATES 13 g	FAT 10 g	CALORIES 286 Calories per serving
	x				

OVEN-BAKED SOLE ON A BED OF RED CHICORY AND WINTER SQUASH

Setup and preparation: Approx. 30 minutes
Baking time: Approx. 25 minutes
Makes 2 servings

INGREDIENTS

- 1 tbsp. oil
- 3 tbsp. white balsamic vinegar (rice or white wine vinegar can be substituted)
- 1 tbsp. liquid honey
- ½ tsp. salt
- 2 heads of red chicory, quartered
- 1lb. (400 g) winter squash, such as butternut or pumpkin, peeled, seeded and diced in ¾" (2 cm) cubes

- 2 skinless sole fillets, 6 ¼ oz. (180 g) each, or 12.5 oz. (360 g) total, approx. ¾ lb. total
- 1 tbsp. lemon juice
- ½ tsp. salt

PREPARATION

1. Preheat the oven to 390° F (200° C). Mix the oil, vinegar, honey, and salt. Place the chicory and winter squash on a baking plate lined with parchment paper. Coat the vegetables with the oil mixture using a brush.

2. Bake for 25 minutes in the middle rung of the oven.

3. Cut the fish fillets in two, and sprinkle with lemon juice and salt. Place on top of the vegetables, and continue baking for 7 minutes.

USEFUL INFORMATION

This dish is low in calories and carbohydrates. It can be easily integrated into a weight-loss or low-carbohydrate diet. This recipe is very high in the antioxidant beta carotene.

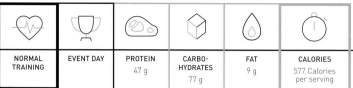

NORMAL TRAINING	EVENT DAY	PROTEIN 47 g	CARBO-HYDRATES 77 g	FAT 9 g	CALORIES 577 Calories per serving

PENNE WITH RAW TOMATO AND GRILLED JUMBO SHRIMP

Setup and preparation: Approx. 30 minutes
Makes 2 servings

INGREDIENTS

- 8 jumbo shrimp tails, peeled (or 20 normal sized shrimp)
- 1 tbsp. olive oil
- 1 garlic clove, finely chopped
- ½ tsp. salt

- 1 ½ oz. (50 g) arugula, finely chopped
- 1 large mild red chili pepper, seeded and finely chopped
- 14 oz. (400 g) fresh tomatoes, peeled (optional), seeded and very finely diced
- ½ c. (one small bunch) fresh basil, finely chopped
- ½ tsp. salt
- pepper, to taste

- 7 oz. (200 g) short pasta, such as penne
- boiling water, salted

PREPARATION

1. Preheat the oven to 140° F (60° C). Heat the oil in a frying pan. Brown the shrimp approx. 1 minute on each side, depending on the size. Add the garlic and continue cooking for 1 minute. Add salt. Transfer into a baking dish and place the oven.

2. For the pasta sauce: mix the arugula, red chili, tomatoes, basil, salt and pepper.

3. Cook the penne in boiling, salted water until al dente. Drain. Mix immediately with the sauce, and top with the shrimp.

USEFUL INFORMATION

This dish is very low in fat. It is the perfect dish to aid in recovery from training.

MUSCLE MASS BUILDING	PROTEIN 56 g	CARBO-HYDRATES 41 g	FAT 25 g	CALORIES 613 Calories per serving

SEA BREAM WITH POTATOES AND SALSA VERDE

Setup and preparation: Approx. 30 minutes
Makes 2 servings

INGREDIENTS

- 2 sea breams, such as organic gilt head sea bream,17.5 oz. (500 g) total, slightly more than 1 lb. total, rinsed inside and out in cold water and dried using a paper towel.
- 1 tbsp. olive oil
- 1 ½ tsp. salt
- pepper, to taste
- 1 organic lemon, sliced
- ¼ c. (one half of a small bunch) fresh basil

- 14 oz. (400 g) waxy baby potatoes, quartered
- 1 tbsp. olive oil
- ½ tsp. salt
- 1 tsp. cayenne pepper or chili powder

- ¼ lb. (100 g) spinach, washed and dried

- 1 bouquet of mixed chopped fresh herbs, such as basil, tarragon, parsley, chives, etc
- 1 organic lemon, grated zest and
- 2 tbsp. of juice
- 1 tbsp. soy sauce
- 1 tbsp. olive oil

PREPARATION

1. Preheat the oven to 390° F (200° C). Baste the fish with olive oil, and season on the inside and out. Fill the inside of the fish with the lemon slices and basil. Place the fish on a baking plate lined with parchment paper.

2. Mix the potatoes with oil, salt, and chili powder. Place on the baking tray around the fish.

3. Bake for 21 minutes on the middle rung of the oven.

4. Mix the spinach in with the potatoes and bake for and additional 4 minutes.

5. While the dish is baking, prepare the salsa verde. Blend the herbs, olive oil, soy sauce, lemon zest and juice with an immersion blender. Let sit for at least 15 minutes.

USEFUL INFORMATION

Suggestions:
- Substitute arugula for the mixed herbs.
- For a gluten-free option: Substitute salt- or gluten-free soy sauce for the the soy sauce.

This dish is particularly rich in protein (57 g per serving). It can be eaten during post-workout recovery after a muscle building session, such as bodybuilding – which can generate muscle aches – and plyometrics. If the training included high-intensity physical activity, complete the meal with a carbohydrate-rich dessert, such as compote, fruit salad, or rice pudding.

MICRO-NUTRIENTS

INTENSE TRAINING

NORMAL TRAINING

PROTEIN
44 g

CARBO-HYDRATES
76 g

FAT
15 g

CALORIES
615 Calories
per serving

COD, SWEET PEPPER RATATOUILLE AND POLENTA

Setup and preparation: Approx. 40 minutes
Makes 2 servings

INGREDIENTS

- 1 tbsp. olive oil
- 1 onion, halved and sliced
- 2 garlic cloves, minced
- 2 red peppers and 3 yellow peppers, cut into thin 1" (2 cm) strips
- 2 tbsp. tomato concentrate

- ½ c. (1 dl) vegetable broth
- 2 sprigs rosemary

- 2 ½ c. (7 dl) vegetable broth
- 5 ½ oz. (150 g) fine cornmeal

- 2 cod filets, 7 oz. (180 g) each
- A small amount of oil for cooking, use as little as possible
- ½ tsp. salt
- pepper, to taste
- 1 lemon, quartered

PREPARATION

1. Heat the oil in a pan. Sauté the onion and garlic until soft. Add the peppers, and cook for 2 minutes, constantly stirring. Add the tomato concentrate, and stir until smooth.

2. Add the broth and the rosemary sprigs, and bring to a boil. Lower the heat and cover. Simmer over medium heat for 10 minutes.

3. In a separate pan, bring the broth to a boil. Add the cornmeal by pouring it slowly into the broth, while stirring constantly. Continue stirring, and cook over medium heat for 4 minutes, until the polenta is thick.

4. Heat some oil in a pan. Lower the heat, and cook the cod filets over medium heat for 4 minutes on each side. Season with salt and pepper, to taste. Serve with lemon wedges, polenta, and ratatouille.

USEFUL INFORMATION

Suggestion:
- Add 4 tbsp. Parmesan cheese to the polenta.

This dish is distinguished by being exceptionally high in various micronutrients, such as the B vitamins, vitamin C, vitamin E, vitamin D, and selenium. As such, it can be consumed during periods of intensive training. The macronutrient content correlates to a medium-sized serving.

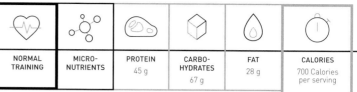

NORMAL TRAINING	MICRO-NUTRIENTS	PROTEIN 45 g	CARBO-HYDRATES 67 g	FAT 28 g	CALORIES 700 Calories per serving

SAUTÉED RICE WITH VEGETABLES AND DICED SALMON

Set up and preparation: Approx. 35 minutes
Makes 2 servings

INGREDIENTS

- 5 ½ oz. (150 g) brown or black rice
- boiling water, salted

- A small amount of oil for cooking, use as little as possible
- 2 garlic cloves, finely chopped
- 1 oz. (20 g) fresh ginger, grated
- 3 ½ oz. (100 g) kale, julienned
- 3 ½ oz. (100 g) broccoli florets
- 3 ½ oz. (100 g) carrots, julienned
- 2 tbsp. soy sauce
- ½ c. water

- 12 ½ oz. (360 g) salmon, diced into ½" (2 cm) cubes, approx. ¾ lb total
- ½ tsp. salt
- 1 tbsp. white or black sesame seeds

- 1 lime, quartered

Ingredients with possible
traces of gluten
x   Soy sauce

PREPARATION

1. Cook the rice, as instructed on the package.

2. Meanwhile, heat the oil in a large frying pan. Lower the heat, and sauté the garlic and ginger until soft. Add the vegetables, and sauté until the kale softens. Add the soy sauce and water, cover, and cook on low heat for 10 minutes.

3. Heat some oil in a frying pan, and cook the diced salmon for 4 minutes, stirring so it cooks evenly on all sides. Season with salt. Roll in the sesame seeds.

4. Mix the vegetables with rice, and adjust the seasoning, if necessary. Top with the diced salmon, and garnish with lime quarters.

USEFUL INFORMATION

Salmon provides a large amount of vitamin D and Omega-3, a type of fat with anti-inflammatory properties. This dish can be enjoyed on normal training days.

HEALTHY SNACKS

| NORMAL TRAINING | MICRO-NUTRIENTS | PROTEIN 35 g | CARBO-HYDRATES 84 g | FAT 19 g | CALORIES 647 Calories per serving |

PORK TENDERLOIN SANDWICH WITH HUMMUS

Setup and preparation: Approx. 30 minutes
Makes 2 servings

INGREDIENTS

- A small amount of oil for cooking, use as little as possible
- 6 oz. (160 g) pork tenderloin, cut into thin strips
- salt and pepper, to taste

- 4 slices of bread, 2 oz. (60 g) per slice, or 1 baguette, 8 oz. (250 g), cut in half into two portions, grilled
- 3 ½ oz. (100 g) hummus
- 1 red onion, thinly sliced into rings
- 1 ½ oz. (40 g) little gem lettuce

PREPARATION

1. Heat the oil in a frying pan. Add the tenderloin strips and cook for 4 minutes, stirring so it browns on all sides. Season with salt and pepper. Remove from pan.

2. Spread hummus on a slice of bread. Top with the sliced onion and lettuce, and add some of the pork mixture. Cover with a second slice of bread.

USEFUL INFORMATION

Suggestion :
- Serve with home-made guacamole.

This sandwich is a well-balanced combination of protein and carbohydrates. It is recommended as a recovery meal. To complete the meal, accompany it with mixed raw vegetables, such as, cherry tomatoes, carrot sticks, bell peppers, and cucumber, as well as yogurt and fruit for dessert. Hummus contains chick peas, which causes digestive discomfort in some people, and is not recommended before competition.

NORMAL TRAINING	PROTEIN 11 g	CARBO-HYDRATES 67 g	FAT 18 g	CALORIES 474 Calories per serving

GUACAMOLE

Setup and preparation: Approx. 30 minutes
Makes 2 servings

INGREDIENTS

- 1 avocado, soft and ripe
- 1 shallot, finely chopped
- 1 tbsp. fresh coriander or parsley, finely chopped
- 1 tbsp. lemon or lime juice
- ½ tsp. salt
- pepper, to taste
- 1 pinch of chili powder or cayenne pepper

- 2 medium-sized pieces of pita
bread, preferably whole wheat, cut
into 8 wedges

PREPARATION

1. Mash the avocado with a fork. Stir in the shallot and coriander or parsley. Season with salt, pepper and chili powder or cayenne.

2. Preheat the oven to 430° F (220° C). Place the pita wedges on a baking tray lined with parchment paper. Bake for 3 minutes. Serve with guacamole.

USEFUL INFORMATION

This great classic is mostly rich in complex carbohydrates and healthy fat. Avocado is rich in heart-healthy monoun-saturated fat – the same as in olive oil – which helps lower inflammation in the body and aids in recovery.

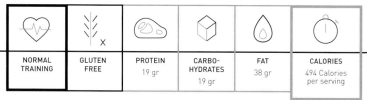

NORMAL TRAINING	GLUTEN FREE	PROTEIN 19 gr	CARBO-HYDRATES 19 gr	FAT 38 gr	CALORIES 494 Calories per serving

TOMATO, MELON AND MOZZARELLA SALAD

Setup and preparation: Approx. 30 minutes
Makes 2 servings

INGREDIENTS

- 2 tbsp. red wine vinegar
- 3 tbsp. olive oil
- salt and pepper, to taste

- 4 tomatoes, quartered
- 1 cantaloupe, diced
- 1 red onion, halved and sliced
- 7 oz. (200 g) celery, diced

- 5 oz. (140 g) mozzarella, in pieces
- ¼ c. (one small bunch) fresh basil, leaves only
- 2 oz. (50 g) arugula

PREPARATION

1. Mix the vinegar, oil, salt, and pepper.

2. Toss the vegetables with the dressing.

3. Mix in the mozzarella, basil, and arugula.

USEFUL INFORMATION

Suggestions:
- Substitute watermelon for the cantaloupe, and feta for the mozzarella
- Substitute walnut oil for the olive oil.

This starter contains many antioxidants and is especially high in vitamin C. It is a good source of calcium and phosphorus, both important in building and maintaining strong bones. It is recommended to pair this starter with a low-fat main dish, such as white fish or grilled chicken skewers.

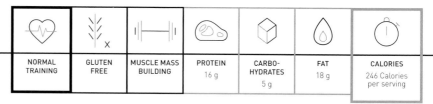

NORMAL TRAINING	GLUTEN FREE	MUSCLE MASS BUILDING	PROTEIN 16 g	CARBO- HYDRATES 5 g	FAT 18 g	CALORIES 246 Calories per serving

SCRAMBLED EGGS WITH TOMATO

Setup and preparation: Approx. 15 minutes
Makes 2 servings

INGREDIENTS

- 1 tbsp. olive oil
- 1 shallot, finely chopped
- 1 tomato, seeded and finely diced

- 4 eggs, beaten
- 2 tbsp. 1% milk
- ½ tsp. salt
- 1 tbsp. fresh chives, finely chopped

PREPARATION

1. Heat the oil in a non-stick frying pan. Sauté the shallot until translucent. Add the diced tomato, and heat for few minutes.

2. Beat the eggs with the milk and salt. Pour into the skillet along with the tomato mixture. Cook over medium heat, stirring with a wooden spoon. Sprinkle with chives and serve immediately.

USEFUL INFORMATION

Suggestion :
- You can prepare this recipe with turkey, spinach, green asparagus, mushrooms, or bell pepper, to name a few suggestions.

This protein-rich meal can be eaten for breakfast, providing the body with a metabolism boost first thing in the morning.

NORMAL TRAINING	EVENT DAY	RECOVERY	PROTEIN 4 g	CARBO-HYDRATES 44 g	FAT 1 g	CALORIES 201 Calories per serving

FRUIT COMPOTE

Setup and preparation: Approx. 30 minutes
Makes 2 servings

INGREDIENTS

- 4 oranges, peeled and wedged
- 2 oz. (60 g) dates, chopped

SUGGESTIONS FOR OTHER FRUIT COMPOTES
- 4 pears, chopped, ½ vanilla bean (1 tsp. vanilla extract), 1 tbsp. honey
- ½ lb (200 g) plums, pitted, 1 tbsp. honey, 1 tsp. cinnamon
- 4 apples, sliced, ½" (1 c) fresh ginger, ½ tsp. cinnamon
- 1 mango, 1 passion fruit

 Ingredients with possible traces of gluten
x Dates

PREPARATION

1. Bring the oranges and dates to a boil. Cook, covered, until the oranges collapse. Mix with an immersion blender.

USEFUL INFORMATION

Prepare large quantities to put in the freezer, divided into individual portions.
Compote can keep in refrigerator, covered, for 4 days.
Compote consists mainly of carbohydrates. It can be enjoyed as a snack after exercise, or as a dessert.

NORMAL TRAINING	RECOVERY	GLUTEN FREE x	PROTEIN 18 g	CARBO-HYDRATES 26 g	FAT 5 g	CALORIES 221 Calories per serving

GREEK YOGURT WITH FRUIT

Setup and preparation: Approx. 30 minutes
Makes 2 servings

INGREDIENTS

- 1 pt. (400 g) fat-free Greek yogurt
- 1 banana
- 3 ½ oz. (100 g) raspberries
- ½ oz. (20 g) flax, chia or sesame seeds, or chopped nuts

SUGGESTIONS
- Substitute blueberries, blackberries, or cherries for the raspberries
- Omit the banana and sweeten the Greek yogurt with 1 tbsp. liquid honey or agave syrup

PREPARATION

1. Mix the Greek yogurt, banana, and raspberries in a blender, and pour into small bowls. Sprinkle with flax seed.

USEFUL INFORMATION

This dish, which contains 18 g protein and 26 grams carbohydrates per serving, is a very good recovery snack. For intensive training or competition, an additional carbohydrate may be added, such as gingerbread, granola, cereal or a muesli bar.

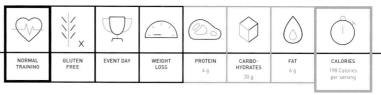

NORMAL TRAINING	GLUTEN FREE x	EVENT DAY	WEIGHT LOSS	PROTEIN 6 g	CARBO-HYDRATES 30 g	FAT 6 g	CALORIES 198 Calories per serving

FRUIT SALAD

Setup and preparation: Approx. 10 minutes
Makes 2 servings

INGREDIENTS

- 1 ¼ c. (300 g) fruit, such as mango, pineapple, or banana, diced into ¾" (2 cm) cubes
- 1 c. (200 g) mixed berries, such as strawberries, blueberries, and raspberries
- 1 pomegranate, seeded
- 1 tbsp. agave syrup
- 2 tbsp. chia seeds
- 2 sprigs of fresh mint or vervain, chopped

PREPARATION

1. Mix the fruit with all the ingredients, including mint, and serve immediately.

USEFUL INFORMATION

Berries are very rich in many vitamins, antioxidants, and nutrients, including polyphenols, which are protective substances. They are very important to include in an athlete's diet.

NORMAL TRAINING	EVENT DAY	WEIGHT LOSS	PROTEIN 11 g	CARBO-HYDRATES 34 g	FAT 3 g	CALORIES 207 Calories per serving

YOGURT WITH GOJI BERRIES

Setup and preparation: Approx.10 minutes
Makes 2 servings

INGREDIENTS

- 1 pt. (400 g) fat-free Greek yogurt, or fat-free plain yogurt)
- 1 banana
- 2 tbsp. goji berries

Ingredients with possible traces of gluten
x goji berries

PREPARATION

1. Mix all ingredients, and allow to sit until the berries have softened. Mix with an immersion blender, and serve immediately.

USEFUL INFORMATION

Suggestion:
- Substitute fat-free cottage cheese for the fat-free yogurt.

Goji berries are very high in antioxidant-rich polyphenols and betaine.

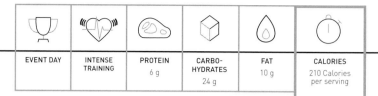

| EVENT DAY | INTENSE TRAINING | PROTEIN 6 g | CARBO-HYDRATES 24 g | FAT 10 g | CALORIES 210 Calories per serving |

GRANOLA

Setup and preparation: Approx. 5 minutes
Baking time: Approx. 15 minutes
Makes approx. 8 servings

INGREDIENTS

- 1 ⅓ c. (300 g) oat flakes
- 1 oz. (30 g) hazelnuts, coarsely chopped
- 1 oz. (30 g) almonds, coarsely chopped
- 1 oz. (30 g) chia seeds
- 1 oz. (30 g) walnuts, coarsely chopped
- 1 tbsp. coconut oil
- 2 tbsp. liquid honey

PREPARATION

1. Preheat oven to 350° F (180° C). Put all the ingredients in a large bowl and stir by hand, until thoroughly mixed. Spread the mixture on a baking tray lined with parchment paper. Bake on the middle rung of the oven for 15 minutes. Stir with a wooden spoon halfway through the baking time, if necessary. Let cool, and store in a sealed container.

USEFUL INFORMATION

Suggestions:
- Ideal with yogurt, muesli, cottage cheese, and fruit.
- Substitute millet or spelt flakes for the oats.

Granola is energy dense and can be eaten before high physical activity and expenditure, such as intense training or competition. It can also be enjoyed as a snack during a hike or on active days. Additionally, it is a healthy, energy-rich breakfast.

EVENT DAY	INTENSE TRAINING	PROTEIN 5 g	CARBO-HYDRATES 24 g	FAT 6 g	CALORIES 170 Calories per slice

BANANA BREAD

Setup and preparations: Approx. 30 minutes
Baking: Approx. 1 hour
Loaf pan, approx. 8 inches, lined in parchment paper
Makes 12 slices

INGREDIENTS

- 1 ½ c. (180 g) plain non-fat yogurt
- 2 eggs, beaten
- 2 tbsp. liquid honey
- 6 ripe bananas, approx. 1.5 lb. (800 g) total
- 1 tbsp. lemon juice
- Pinch salt

- ½ c. (100 g) mixed nuts, such as hazelnuts, walnuts, or almonds
- 3 ½ oz. (100 g) wholemeal spelt flour
- 2 tsp. baking powder

PREPARATION

1. Mix the yogurt, eggs, honey, bananas, lemon juice and salt in a blender.

2. Preheat the oven to 350° (180° C). Combine the nuts, flour, and baking powder, and slowly stir it into the yogurt mixture. Pour into a loaf pan. Bake for approx. 1 hour. on the center rung of the oven. Remove it from the oven. Once it cools down slightly, remove the bread from the loaf pan. Place on a cooling rack, until it arrives at room temperature.

USEFUL INFORMATION

Banana bread contains very high levels of carbohydrates. It can be eaten when energy needs are high, such as during intense training, recovery, or carbo-loading in preparation for a competition.

Suggestion:
The use of wholemeal flour may cause digestive discomfort in some people. If this applies to you, replace the wholemeal flour with refined flour.

EVENT DAY	INTENSE TRAINING	PROTEIN 5 g	CARBO-HYDRATES 27 g	FAT 10 g	CALORIES 218 Calories per serving

ENERGY BAR

Setup and preparation: Approx. 10 minutes
Baking: Approx. 20 minutes
Makes 8 bars

INGREDIENTS

- 4 tbsp. liquid honey
- 2 tbsp. sugar
- 2 tbsp. coconut oil

- 4 ¼ oz. (120 g) oats
- 1 ¾ oz. (50 g) sesame seeds
- 1 ¾ oz. (50 g) chia seeds
- 1 ¾ oz. (50 g) goji berries

PREPARATION

1. Bring the honey, coconut oil and sugar to a boil.

2. Add the oats, seeds and berries, and stir well.

3. Preheat oven to 340° F (170° C). Spread the mixture evenly and compactly on a rectangular cooking sheet lined with parchment paper so that it is ¾" (2 cm) thick.

4. Bake for approx. 20 minutes.

5. Remove from the oven. Cool slightly. While the mixture is still warm, cut into 8 bars. Store in a sealed, airtight box, for 6 days.

USEFUL INFORMATION

These energy bars can be enjoyed as a snack one to two hours before exercise.
Although these bars are slightly more caloric than store-bought varieties, they contain more B vitamins. B vitamins play a large role in metabolizing carbohydrates and energy production.

NORMAL TRAINING	GLUTEN FREE	EVENT DAY	RECOVERY	PROTEIN 8 g	CARBO-HYDRATES 49 g	FAT 3 g	CALORIES 255 Calories per serving

RICE PUDDING

Setup and preparation: Approx. 35 minutes
Makes 2 servings

INGREDIENTS

- 1 ½ c. (3 dl) skim milk
- 2 ½ oz. (75 g) round rice, such as arborio
- 1 vanilla pod, split lengthwise, seeded (or 2 tsp. vanilla extract)
- 1 tbsp. liquid honey
- Pinch of salt

- 1 passion fruit, pulped

PREPARATION

1. Bring the milk to a boil with all the ingredients, including salt. Simmer over medium heat for 20 minutes, stirring often. Serve with the passion fruit pulp.

USEFUL INFORMATION

Suggestion:
- Serve with fruit compote or sprinkle with cinnamon.

Each portion carries approx. 50 g of carbohydrates. It can be eaten as a dessert or for recovery after exercise; it must be paired with a protein source.

RECOVERY	PROTEIN 1 g	CARBO- HYDRATES 6 g	FAT 2 g	CALORIES 46 Calories per cookie

PEANUT BUTTER COOKIES

Setup and preparation: Approx. 10 minutes
Baking time: Approx. 20 minutes
Serves 30 units

INGREDIENTS

- 3 ripe bananas, mashed
- 3 ½ oz. (100 g) oats
- 1 ¾ oz. (50 g) dark chocolate, finely diced (or chocolate chips)
- 3 tbsp. peanut butter

PREPARATION

1. Combine the ingredients using an electric mixer. Take a spoonful of dough and place it on a baking tray lined with parchment paper. Continue with the remainder of the dough, leaving 1" (3 cm) between each cookie.

2. Preheat the oven to 350° F (180° C). Bake for approx. 20 minutes in the center rung of the oven Remove. Let cool on a cooling rack.

USEFUL INFORMATION

These cookies provide energy for exercise and are an excellent, healthy pre-workout or afternoon snack.

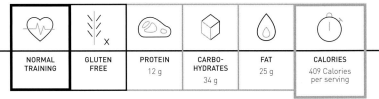

NORMAL TRAINING	GLUTEN FREE	PROTEIN 12 g	CARBO-HYDRATES 34 g	FAT 25 g	CALORIES 409 Calories per serving

LIGHT PANNA COTTA

Setup and preparation: Approx. 30 minutes
Chilling time: Approx. 4 hours
Amount : for 4 small jars of approx. ½ c. (1.5 dl) each, or 2 jars of 8 oz. (3 dl) each

INGREDIENTS

- 1 c. (2.5 dl) light cream (15%)
- 1 c. (2.5 dl) 1% or 2 % milk
- 2 tbsp. sugar
- 1 vanilla bean, slit, seeded (or 2 tsp. vanilla extract)

- 2 gelatin sheets, previously soaked for 5 min. in cold water, or one packet powdered gelatin, prepared according to instructions on the package

- 9 oz. (250 g) mixed berries
- 1 tbsp. powdered sugar or agave syrup
- 1 tbsp. lemon juice

PREPARATION

1. Bring the cream, milk, sugar and vanilla to a boil. Simmer uncovered until approx. 1 ⅔ c. (4 dl) liquid remains.

2. Add the prepared gelatin to the cream mixture. Stir well with a whisk until dissolved. Pass the mixture through a fine sieve into a container with a spout. Place glasses or mason jars on a clean cloth, and fill with the mixture. Leave to cool, then refrigerate, covered, for 4 hours.

3. For the coulis: mix the berries, sugar and lemon juice with an immersion blender.

4. Pour a little coulis on top of each panna cotta.

USEFUL INFORMATION

Although this dessert is quite high in calories, the berries are rich in fiber, vitamin C, phytonutrients, and antioxidants, which are very protective for athletes training at a high level.

MICRO-NUTRIENTS	GLUTEN FREE	PROTEIN 3 g	CARBO-HYDRATES 26 g	FAT 7 g	CALORIES 179 Calories per serving

GREEN SMOOTHIE

Setup and preparation: 5 minutes
Makes 2 servings, 8 oz. (240 ml) per serving

INGREDIENTS

- 1 ¾ oz. (50 g) frozen or fresh pineapple, cut into 5 chunks
- ¼ oz. (7 g) raw spinach, approximately one handful
- ¼ oz. (7 g) raw kale, approximately one handful
- ¼ avocado
- 1 banana
- 8 oz. (240 ml) almond milk
- 1 oz. (30 ml) water
- 4 ice cubes

PREPARATION

1. Place all ingredients in a blender.

2. Blend on highest speed until smooth.

USEFUL INFORMATION

You can drink the green smoothie at anytime to promote alkalinity and good health. For breakfast, it will provide vitamins, minerals, antioxidants, and healthy fat to energize the body and improve concentration in the morning.

WEIGHT TRAINING	PROTEIN 8 g	CARBO-HYDRATES 28 g	FAT 13 g	CALORIES 261 Calories per serving

PEANUT BUTTER SMOOTHIE

Set up and preparation : approx. 5 min
Makes 2 servings, 8 oz. (480 ml) per serving

INGREDIENTS

- 3 tablespoons natural peanut butter
- 1 banana
- 8 oz. (240 ml) almond milk
- 1 tsp. ground flax seeds
- 4-5 ice cubes

PREPARATION

1. Place all ingredients in a blender.

2. Blend on highest speed until smooth.

USEFUL INFORMATION

This high-energy, body-mass building smoothie is a great snack or mini-meal during the day, providing healthy fat, protein, calcium, and vitamin D.

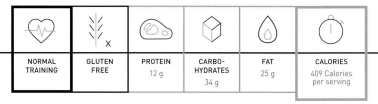

NORMAL TRAINING	GLUTEN FREE	PROTEIN 12 g	CARBO-HYDRATES 34 g	FAT 25 g	CALORIES 409 Calories per serving

LIGHT PANNA COTTA

Setup and preparation: Approx. 30 minutes
Chilling time: Approx. 4 hours
Amount : for 4 small jars of approx. ½ c. (1.5 dl) each, or 2 jars of 8 oz. (3 dl) each

INGREDIENTS

- 1 c. (2.5 dl) light cream (15%)
- 1 c. (2.5 dl) 1% or 2 % milk
- 2 tbsp. sugar
- 1 vanilla bean, slit, seeded (or 2 tsp. vanilla extract)

- 2 gelatin sheets, previously soaked for 5 min. in cold water, or one packet powdered gelatin, prepared according to instructions on the package

- 9 oz. (250 g) mixed berries
- 1 tbsp. powdered sugar or agave syrup
- 1 tbsp. lemon juice

PREPARATION

1. Bring the cream, milk, sugar and vanilla to a boil. Simmer uncovered until approx. 1 ⅔ c. (4 dl) liquid remains.

2. Add the prepared gelatin to the cream mixture. Stir well with a whisk until dissolved. Pass the mixture through a fine sieve into a container with a spout. Place glasses or mason jars on a clean cloth, and fill with the mixture. Leave to cool, then refrigerate, covered, for 4 hours.

3. For the coulis: mix the berries, sugar and lemon juice with an immersion blender.

4. Pour a little coulis on top of each panna cotta.

USEFUL INFORMATION

Although this dessert is quite high in calories, the berries are rich in fiber, vitamin C, phytonutrients, and antioxidants, which are very protective for athletes training at a high level.

RECOVERY	GLUTEN FREE	PROTEIN 7 g	CARBO-HYDRATES 28 g	FAT 10 g	CALORIES 230 Calories per serving

PINK SMOOTHIE

Setup and preparation: Approx. 5 minutes
Makes 2 servings, 8 oz. (480 ml) per serving

INGREDIENTS

- 6 strawberries, frozen or fresh
- 1 ¾ oz. (50 g) mango, cut into 5 chunks
- 1 banana
- 6 oz. (180 ml) almond milk
- 4 tbsp. non-fat Greek yogurt (or other high-protein plain yogurt)
- 1 tsp. chia seeds
- 4 ice cubes

PREPARATION

1. Place all ingredients in a blender.

2. Blend on highest speed until smooth.

USEFUL INFORMATION

This protein-rich smoothie is perfect as an afternoon snack or after training. It provides the building blocks for strong bones and muscles.

INTENSE TRAINING	RECOVERY	PROTEIN 3 g	CARBO-HYDRATES 25 g	FAT 3 g	CALORIES 139 Calories per serving

SUPER-BERRY SMOOTHIE

Setup and preparation: Approx. 5 minutes
Makes 2 servings, 8 oz. (480 ml) per serving

INGREDIENTS

- ½ c. (120 ml) blueberries, frozen or fresh
- 4 strawberries, frozen or fresh
- 1 small banana, 3 ½ oz. (100g)
- 2 oz. (60 ml) tart cherry juice
- ¼ oz. (8 g) raw spinach, one small handful
- 1 tsp. chia seeds
- 4 oz. (120 ml) coconut water

PREPARATION

1. Place all ingredients in a blender.

2. Blend on highest speed until smooth.

USEFUL INFORMATION

This smoothie is great to have after intense training. The tart cherry juice, Omega-3, and high antioxidant content will bring down inflammation and promote recovery and healing.

RECOVERY	GLUTEN FREE	PROTEIN 3 g	CARBO-HYDRATES 20 g	FAT 3 g	CALORIES 119 Calories per serving

TROPICAL SMOOTHIE

Setup and preparation: Approx. 5 minutes
Makes 2 servings, 8 oz. (480 ml) per serving

INGREDIENTS

- 2 oz. (60 g) pineapple, fresh or frozen, cut into 7 chunks
- 1 ½ oz. (40 g) mango, frozen or fresh, cut into 4 chunks
- ½ banana
- 4 tbsp. non-fat Greek yogurt (or other high protein plain yogurt)
- 2 oz. (60 ml) pineapple juice
- 4 oz. (120 ml) coconut water
- 4 ice cubes

PREPARATION

1. Place all ingredients in a blender.

2. Blend on highest speed until smooth.

USEFUL INFORMATION

This smoothie is great to have at anytime of the day to promote recovery. It provides the body with many nutrients and electrolytes, such as potassium. Pineapples and pineapple juice contain natural bromelain enzymes that help reduce swelling and inflammation throughout the body. This smoothie's high vitamin C content boosts immunity and promotes tissue and muscle repair.

ADDITIONAL INFORMATION

MACRONUTRIENTS   Recipe ranking in terms of **protein**: P=Protein, F=Fat, C=Carbohydrates, kJ=Kilojoules, Cal=Calories

RECIPE	PAGE	PER SERVING				
		kJ	Cal	P	F	C
Duck Breast with Brussels Sprouts and Quinoa	56	3921	938	59	34	99
Pasta with Broccoli, Squash and Chicken	48	3018	722	59	18	81
Chopped Veal with Pasta, Kale and Goat Cheese	76	3858	923	57	23	122
Sea Bream with Potatoes and Salsa Verde	106	2562	613	56	25	41
Vegetable and Beef Lasagna	64	3787	906	56	22	121
Stuffed Veal Cutlets with Carrot Purée	74	1965	470	54	18	23
Chicken and Vegetable Couscous	46	2742	656	54	16	74
Chicken and Bulgur Salad	54	3950	945	52	37	101
Pork Tenderloin with Quinoa and Vegetables	84	2646	633	51	17	69
Athlete's Niçoise Salad	88	2299	550	50	26	29
Warm Rice Salad with Turkey	50	4489	1074	48	58	90
Penne with Raw Tomato and Grilled Jumbo Shrimp	104	2412	577	47	9	77
Lentil Salad with Veal	78	3511	840	46	44	65
Baked Sweet Potatoes Stuffed with Lean Ground Beef	70	2696	645	46	13	86
Meatballs in Tomato Sauce	68	3122	747	46	23	89
Asian Soup with Soba Noodles and Chicken	44	1777	425	46	5	49
Salmon Caesar Salad with Kale	92	2817	674	46	42	28
Sautéed Rice with Vegetables and Diced Salmon	110	2926	700	45	28	67
Pork Tenderloin with Peppered Tofu	82	1868	447	45	23	15
Veal Cutlets with Lemon Risotto and Fennel Salad	80	3992	955	45	47	88
Chicken Stew with Fennel, Asparagus and Polenta	60	3097	741	45	21	93
Cod, Sweet Pepper Ratatouille and Polenta	108	2571	615	44	15	76
Salmon with Mango Salsa and Farro	100	2767	662	44	30	54
Braised Chicken and Sweet Potato Purée	52	2253	539	43	15	58

in grams

RECIPE	PAGE	kJ	Cal	P	F	C
Chili con Carne	72	1848	442	42	14	37
Turkey Cutlets with Roasted Winter Squash	58	1296	310	41	10	14
White Bean Salad with Avocado and Shrimp	98	2449	586	41	34	29
Sautéed Beef with Green Asparagus and Brown Rice	66	2579	617	39	25	59
Red Potato Salad with Calamari	94	2161	517	39	17	52
Oven-Baked Sole on a Bed of Red Chicory and Winter Squash	102	1195	286	37	10	13
Vegetable and Beef Salad	62	1413	338	37	19	12
Beetroot Salad with Pears and Goji Berries, Grilled Sole	96	2057	492	37	24	32
Pork Tenderloin Sandwich with Hummus	114	2704	647	35	19	84
Ginger and Orange Carrot Soup with Scallops	90	1622	388	30	16	31
Tomato, Melon and Mozzarella Salad	118	2065	494	19	38	19
Greek yogurt with fruit	122	924	221	18	5	26
Scrambled Eggs with Tomato	120	1028	246	16	18	5
Light Panna Cotta	136	1710	409	12	25	34
Yogurt with Goji Berries	124	865	207	11	3	34
Guacamole	116	1981	474	11	18	67
Peanut Butter Smoothie	138	1091	261	8	13	28
Rice Pudding	132	1066	255	8	3	49
Pink Smoothie	140	961	230	7	10	28
Granola	126	878	210	6	10	24
Fruit Salad	124	828	198	6	6	30
Energy Bar	130	911	218	5	10	27
Banana Bread	128	711	170	5	6	24
Fruit Compote	122	840	201	4	1	44
Green Smoothie	138	748	179	3	7	26
Super-Berry Smoothie	140	581	139	3	3	25
Tropical Smoothie	142	497	119	3	3	20
Peanut Butter Cookies	134	192	46	1	2	6

in grams

Recipe ranking in terms of **fat**: F=Fat, P=Protein, C=Carbohydrates, kJ=Kilojoules, Cal=Calories

RECIPE	PAGE	PER SERVING				
		kJ	Cal	P	F	C
Warm Rice Salad with Turkey	50	4489	1074	48	58	90
Veal Cutlets with Lemon Risotto and Fennel Salad	80	3992	955	45	47	88
Lentil Salad with Veal	79	3511	840	46	44	65
Salmon Caesar Salad with Kale	92	2817	674	46	42	28
Tomato, Melon and Mozzarella Salad	118	2065	494	19	38	19
Chicken and Bulgur Salad	54	3950	945	52	37	101
Duck Breast with Brussels Sprouts and Quinoa	56	3921	938	59	34	99
White Bean Salad with Avocado and Shrimp	98	2449	586	41	34	29
Salmon with Mango Salsa and Farro	100	2767	662	44	30	54
Sautéed Rice with Vegetables and Diced Salmon	111	2926	700	45	28	67
Athlete's Niçoise Salad	88	2299	550	50	26	29
Sautéed Beef with Green Asparagus and Brown Rice	66	2579	617	39	25	59
Sea Bream with Potatoes and Salsa Verde	106	2562	613	56	25	41
Light Panna Cotta	136	1710	409	12	25	34
Beetroot Salad with Pears and Goji Berries, Grilled Sole	96	2057	492	37	24	32
Meatballs in Tomato Sauce	68	3122	747	46	23	89
Pork Tenderloin with Peppered Tofu	82	1868	447	45	23	15
Chopped Veal with Pasta, Kale and Goat Cheese	76	3858	923	57	23	122
Vegetable and Beef Lasagna	64	3787	906	56	22	121
Chicken Stew with Fennel, Asparagus and Polenta	60	3097	741	45	21	93
Vegetable and Beef Salad	62	1413	338	37	19	12
Pork Tenderloin Sandwich with Hummus	114	2704	647	35	19	84
Guacamole	116	1981	474	11	18	67
Stuffed Veal Cutlets with Carrot Purée	74	1965	470	54	18	23

in grams

RECIPE	PAGE	kJ	Cal	P	F	C
Pasta with Broccoli, Squash and Chicken	48	3018	722	59	18	81
Scrambled Eggs with Tomato	116	1028	246	16	18	5
Red Potato Salad with Calamari	94	2161	517	39	17	52
Pork Tenderloin with Quinoa and Vegetables	84	2646	633	51	17	69
Chicken and Vegetable Couscous	46	2742	656	54	16	74
Ginger and Orange Carrot Soup with Scallops	90	1622	388	30	16	31
Cod, Sweet Pepper Ratatouille and Polenta	108	2571	615	44	15	76
Braised Chicken and Sweet Potato Purée	52	2253	539	43	15	58
Chili con Carne	72	1848	442	42	14	37
Baked Sweet Potatoes Stuffed with Lean Ground Beef	70	2696	645	46	13	86
Peanut Butter Smoothie	138	1091	261	8	13	28
Oven-Baked Sole on a Bed of Red Chicory and Winter Squash	102	1195	286	37	10	13
Granola	126	878	210	6	10	24
Turkey Cutlets with Roasted Winter Squash	58	1296	310	41	10	14
Energy Bar	130	911	218	5	10	27
Pink Smoothie	140	961	230	7	10	28
Penne with Raw Tomato and Grilled Jumbo Shrimp	104	2412	577	47	9	77
Green Smoothie	138	748	179	3	7	26
Banana Bread	128	711	170	5	6	24
Fruit Salad	124	828	198	6	6	30
Greek Yogurt with Fruit	122	924	221	18	5	26
Asian Soup with Soba Noodles and Chicken	44	1777	425	46	5	49
Yogurt with Goji Berries	124	865	207	11	3	34
Super-Berry Smoothie	140	581	139	3	3	25
Tropical Smoothie	142	497	119	3	3	20
Rice Pudding	132	1066	255	8	3	49
Peanut Butter Cookies	134	192	46	1	2	6
Fruit Compote	122	840	201	4	1	44

in grams

Recipe ranking in terms of **Carbohydrates**: C=Carbohydrates, P=Protein, C=Carbohydrates, kJ=Kilojoules, Cal=Calories

RECIPE	PAGE	PER SERVING				
		kJ	Cal	P	F	C
Chopped Veal with Pasta, Kale and Goat Cheese	76	3858	923	57	23	122
Vegetable and Beef Lasagna	64	3787	906	56	22	121
Chicken and Bulgur Salad	54	3950	945	52	37	101
Duck Breast with Brussels Sprouts and Quinoa	56	3921	938	59	34	99
Chicken Stew with Fennel, Asparagus and Polenta	60	3097	741	45	21	93
Warm Rice Salad with Turkey	50	4489	1074	48	58	90
Meatballs in Tomato Sauce	68	3122	747	46	23	89
Veal Cutlets with Lemon Risotto and Fennel Salad	80	3992	955	45	47	88
Baked Sweet Potatoes Stuffed with Lean Ground Beef	70	2696	645	46	13	86
Pork Tenderloin Sandwich with Hummus	114	2704	647	35	19	84
Pasta with Broccoli, Squash and Chicken	48	3018	722	59	18	81
Penne with Raw Tomato and Grilled Jumbo Shrimp	104	2412	577	47	9	77
Cod, Sweet Pepper Ratatouille and Polenta	108	2571	615	44	15	76
Chicken and Vegetable Couscous	46	2742	656	54	16	74
Pork Tenderloin with Quinoa and Vegetables	84	2646	633	51	17	69
Sautéed Rice with Vegetables and Diced Salmon	110	2926	700	45	28	67
Guacamole	116	1981	474	11	18	67
Lentil Salad with Veal	79	3511	840	46	44	65
Sautéed Beef with Green Asparagus and Brown Rice	110	2579	617	39	25	59
Braised Chicken and Sweet Potato Purée	52	2253	539	43	15	58
Salmon with Mango Salsa and Farro	100	2767	662	44	30	54
Red Potato Salad with Calamari	94	2161	517	39	17	52
Rice Pudding	132	1066	255	8	3	49

in grams

RECIPE	PAGE	kJ	Cal	P	F	C
Asian Soup with Soba Noodles and Chicken	44	1777	425	46	5	49
Fruit Compote	122	840	201	4	1	44
Sea Bream with Potatoes and Salsa Verde	106	2562	613	56	25	41
Chili con Carne	72	1848	442	42	14	37
Yogurt with Goji Berries	124	865	207	11	3	34
Light Panna Cotta	136	1710	409	12	25	34
Beetroot Salad with Pears and Goji Berries, Grilled Sole	96	2057	492	37	24	32
Ginger and Orange Carrot Soup with Scallops	90	1622	388	30	16	31
Fruit Salad	124	828	198	6	6	30
White Bean Salad with Avocado and Shrimp	98	2449	586	41	34	29
Athlete's Niçoise Salad	88	2299	550	50	26	29
Salmon Caesar Salad with Kale	92	2817	674	46	42	28
Peanut Butter Smoothie	138	1091	261	8	13	28
Pink Smoothie	140	961	230	7	10	28
Energy Bar	130	911	218	5	10	27
Greek Yogurt with Fruit	122	924	221	18	5	26
Green Smoothie	138	748	179	3	7	26
Super-Berry Smoothie	140	581	139	3	3	25
Granola	126	878	210	6	10	24
Banana Bread	129	711	170	5	6	24
Stuffed Veal Cutlets with Carrot Purée	74	1965	470	54	18	23
Tropical Smoothie	142	497	119	3	3	20
Tomato, Melon and Mozzarella Salad	118	2065	494	19	38	19
Pork Tenderloin with Peppered Tofu	82	1868	447	45	23	15
Turkey Cutlets with Roasted Winter Squash	59	1296	310	41	10	14
Oven-Baked Sole on a Bed of Red Chicory and Winter Squash	102	1195	286	37	10	13
Vegetable and Beef Salad	62	1413	338	37	19	12
Peanut Butter Cookies	134	192	46	1	2	6
Scrambled Eggs with Tomato	120	1028	246	16	18	5

in grams

RECIPE	PAGE	PER PERSON		
		kJ	Cal	VIT C
Cod, Sweet Pepper Ratatouille and Polenta	108	2571	615	370%
Vegetable and Beef Lasagna	64	3787	906	149%
Duck Breast with Brussels Sprouts and Quinoa	64	3921	938	141%
Stuffed Veal Cutlets with Carrot Purée	74	1965	470	115%
Fruit Compote	122	840	201	109%
Fruit Salad	124	828	198	106%
Pasta with Broccoli, Squash and Chicken	48	3018	722	84%
Baked Sweet Potatoes Stuffed with Lean Ground Beef	70	2696	645	83%
Light Panna Cotta	136	1710	409	80%
Lentil Salad with Veal	78	3511	840	73%
Vegetable and Beef Salad	62	1413	338	69%
Pork Tenderloin with Peppered Tofu	82	1868	447	65%
Tomato, Melon and Mozzarella Salad	118	2065	494	65%
White Bean Salad with Avocado and Shrimp	98	2449	586	62%
Athlete's Niçoise Salad	88	2299	550	59%
Salmon with Mango Salsa and Farro	100	2767	662	57%
Chicken and Bulgur Salad	54	3950	945	54%
Braised Chicken and Sweet Potato Purée	52	2253	539	54%
Chopped Veal with Pasta, Kale and Goat Cheese	76	3858	923	53%
Warm Rice Salad with Turkey	50	4489	1074	52%
Super-Berry Smoothie	140	581	139	44%
Chili con Carne	72	1848	442	38%
Pink Smoothie	140	961	230	37%
Sautéed Rice with Vegetables and Diced Salmon	110	2926	700	36%

RECIPE	PAGE	kJ	Cal	VIT C
Ginger and Orange Carrot Soup with Scallops	90	1622	388	35%
Beetroot Salad with Pears and Goji Berries, Grilled Sole	96	2057	492	32%
Penne with Raw Tomato and Grilled Jumbo Shrimp	104	2412	577	29%
Sea Bream with Potatoes and Salsa Verde	106	2562	613	27%
Salmon Caesar Salad with Kale	92	2817	674	27%
Chicken Stew with Fennel, Asparagus and Polenta	60	3097	741	25%
Red Potato Salad with Calamari	94	2161	517	25%
Pork Tenderloin with Quinoa and Vegetables	84	2646	633	21%
Tropical Smoothie	142	497	119	20%
Sautéed Beef with Green Asparagus and Brown Rice	66	2579	617	19%
Chicken and Vegetable Couscous	46	2742	656	18%
Guacamole	116	1981	474	17%
Greek Yogurt with Fruit	122	924	221	17%
Yogurt with Goji Berries	124	865	207	15%
Meatballs in Tomato Sauce	68	3122	747	15%
Asian Soup with Soba Noodles and Chicken	44	1777	425	14%
Scrambled Eggs with Tomato	120	1028	246	13%
Green Smoothie	138	748	179	12%
Veal Cutlets with Lemon Risotto and Fennel Salad	80	3992	955	10%
Rice Pudding	132	1066	255	9%
Energy Bar	130	911	218	5%
Banana Bread	128	711	170	5%
Peanut Butter Smoothie	138	1091	261	4%
Oven-Baked Sole on a Bed of Red Chicory and Winter Squash	102	1195	286	4%
Pork Tenderloin Sandwich with Hummus	114	2704	647	3%
Turkey Cutlets with Roasted Winter Squash	58	1296	310	3%
Peanut Butter Cookies	134	192	46	1%
Granola	126	878	210	0,16%

IRON Values are expressed in % of Recommended Daily Allowance (RDA) (see page 40)

RECIPE	PAGE	PER PERSON kJ	Cal	Iron
Duck Breast with Brussels Sprouts and Quinoa	56	3921	938	111%
Pork Tenderloin with Quinoa and Vegetables	84	2646	633	94%
Meatballs in Tomato Sauce	68	3122	747	83%
Chili con Carne	72	1848	442	72%
Baked Sweet Potatoes Stuffed with Lean Ground Beef	70	2696	645	68%
Lentil Salad with Veal	78	3511	840	58%
Sautéed Beef with Green Asparagus and Brown Rice	66	2579	617	57%
Vegetable and Beef Lasagna	64	3787	906	57%
Pasta with Broccoli, Squash and Chicken	48	3018	722	53%
White Bean Salad with Avocado and Shrimp	98	2449	586	50%
Vegetable and Beef Salad	62	1413	338	47%
Chicken Stew with Fennel, Asparagus and Polenta	60	3097	741	44%
Salmon Caesar Salad with Kale	92	2817	674	41%
Pork Tenderloin with Peppered Tofu	82	1868	447	40%
Cod, Sweet Pepper Ratatouille and Polenta	108	2571	615	39%
Athlete's Niçoise Salad	88	2299	550	37%
Beetroot Salad with Pears and Goji Berries, Grilled Sole	96	2057	492	32%
Pork Tenderloin Sandwich with Hummus	114	2704	647	32%
Ginger and Orange Carrot Soup with Scallops	90	1622	388	32%
Penne with Raw Tomato and Grilled Jumbo Shrimp	104	2412	577	31%
Veal Cutlets with Lemon Risotto and Fennel Salad	80	3992	955	31%
Stuffed Veal Cutlets with Carrot Purée	74	1965	470	29%
Salmon with Mango Salsa and Farro	100	2767	662	27%

RECIPE	PAGE	kJ	Cal	Iron
Sautéed Rice with Vegetables and Diced Salmon	110	2926	700	24%
Sea Bream with Potatoes and Salsa Verde	106	2562	613	24%
Braised Chicken and Sweet Potato Purée	52	2253	539	24%
Turkey Cutlets with Roasted Winter Squash	58	1296	310	24%
Chopped Veal with Pasta, Kale and Goat Cheese		3858	923	24%
Warm Rice Salad with Turkey	50	4489	1074	22%
Chicken and Bulgur Salad	54	3950	945	20%
Scrambled Eggs with Tomato	120	1028	246	19%
Asian Soup with Soba Noodles and Chicken	44	1777	425	18%
Energy Bar	130	911	218	17%
Guacamole	126	1981	474	17%
Red Potato Salad with Calamari	94	2161	517	16%
Chicken and Vegetable Couscous	46	2742	656	15%
Granola	126	878	210	15%
Yogurt with Goji Berries	124	865	207	13%
Tomato, Melon and Mozzarella Salad	118	2065	494	13%
Oven-Baked Sole on a Bed of Red Chicory and Winter Squash	102	1195	286	12%
Light Panna Cotta	136	1710	409	11%
Greek Yogurt with Fruit	122	924	221	11%
Fruit Salad	124	828	198	11%
Fruit Compote	122	840	201	9%
Banana Bread	128	711	170	7%
Super-Berry Smoothie	140	581	139	7%
Peanut Butter Smoothie	138	1091	261	6%
Tropical Smoothie	142	497	119	4%
Green Smoothie	138	748	179	4%
Pink Smoothie	140	961	230	4%
Rice Pudding	132	1066	255	4%
Peanut Butter Cookies	134	192	46	3%

RECIPE	PAGE	PER PERSON		
		kJ	Cal	Mg
Pork Tenderloin with Quinoa and Vegetables	84	2646	633	99%
Duck Breast with Brussels Sprouts and Quinoa	56	3921	938	79%
Warm Rice Salad with Turkey	50	4489	1074	63%
Pasta with Broccoli, Squash and Chicken	48	3018	722	51%
Cod, Sweet Pepper Ratatouille and Polenta	108	2571	615	51%
Sautéed Rice with Vegetables and Diced Salmon	110	2926	700	47%
Pork Tenderloin with Peppered Tofu	82	1868	447	47%
White Bean Salad with Avocado and Shrimp	98	2449	586	46%
Baked Sweet Potatoes Stuffed with Lean Ground Beef	70	2696	645	45%
Meatballs in Tomato Sauce	68	3122	747	41%
Red Potato Salad with Calamari	118	2161	517	38%
Sautéed Beef with Green Asparagus and Brown Rice	66	2579	617	36%
Ginger and Orange Carrot Soup with Scallops	90	1622	388	35%
Chili con Carne	72	1848	442	34%
Vegetable and Beef Lasagna	64	3787	906	32%
Chicken and Vegetable Couscous	46	2742	656	31%
Salmon Caesar Salad with Kale	92	2817	674	31%
Sea Bream with Potatoes and Salsa Verde	106	2562	613	31%
Penne with Raw Tomato and Grilled Jumbo Shrimp	104	2412	577	30%
Braised Chicken and Sweet Potato Purée	52	2253	539	29%
Salmon with Mango Salsa and Farro	100	2767	662	29%
Stuffed Veal Cutlets with Carrot Purée	74	1965	470	28%
Athlete's Niçoise Salad	88	2299	550	28%
Turkey Cutlets with Roasted Winter Squash	58	1296	310	26%

RECIPE	PAGE	kJ	Cal	Mg
Greek Yogurt with Fruit	122	924	221	25%
Beetroot Salad with Pears and Goji Berries, Grilled Sole	96	2057	492	24%
Tomato, Melon and Mozzarella Salad	118	2065	494	24%
Chicken Stew with Fennel, Asparagus and Polenta	60	3097	741	23%
Chicken and Bulgur Salad	54	3950	945	22%
Asian Soup with Soba Noodles and Chicken	44	1777	425	21%
Lentil Salad with Veal	78	3511	840	21%
Pork Tenderloin Sandwich with Hummus	114	2704	647	20%
Peanut Butter Smoothie	140	1091	261	18%
Veal Cutlets with Lemon Risotto and Fennel Salad	80	3992	955	17%
Yogurt with Goji Berries	124	865	207	16%
Oven-Baked Sole on a Bed of Red Chicory and Winter Squash	102	1195	286	14%
Granola	126	878	210	14%
Guacamole	116	1981	474	14%
Fruit Compote	122	840	201	13%
Light Panna Cotta	136	1710	409	13%
Energy Bar	130	911	218	12%
Super-Berry Smoothie	140	581	139	12%
Banana Bread	128	711	170	11%
Tropical Smoothie	142	497	119	11%
Fruit Salad	124	828	198	11%
Chopped Veal with Pasta, Kale and Goat Cheese	76	3858	923	10%
Green Smoothie	138	748	179	10%
Pink Smoothie	140	961	230	9%
Vegetable and Beef Salad	62	1413	338	8%
Scrambled Eggs with Tomato	120	1028	246	7%
Rice Pudding	132	1066	255	7%
Peanut Butter Cookies	134	192	46	4%

INDEX

ACKNOWLEDGMENTS

Our deepest gratitude to all those who have
encouraged us on this journey, in particular:

Cyril Lorenzi, Les pêcheries, in Menton
Diane Cereja
Dr Catherine Garrel, biologist, CHU Grenoble
E.B.H. - Arts de la Table, Nice
Lionel Ritzenthaler
Marie-Laure and Frédérique MORA, Arom Groupe,
Monaco
Pascal Silman, Chef, Monaco
Dr. Stéphane Walrand, INRA Research Director
Théobald Vonblon
Zepter Monaco

© **Edition** Sport @ Food @ Health
Photos: Olivier Remualdo, Nice
Food styling: Andrea Mäusli, Foodstyling, Zurich
Recipes: Andrea Mäusli Foodstyling Zurich,
Switzerland, Eléonore Schoettel, Cap Azur Production,
Cap d'Ail, France
Translations: Natasha Frost, Cap d'Ail, France
Copy Editing and Proofreading: Michelle Perino,
Milan, Italy
Layout, Graphic Design: Minsk Studio, Paris
Printing: Kapp Graphic, Evreux, France
Website Consultancy: Scott Leslie, Monaco Deploy,
Monaco
www.recipesforchampions.com
Videos: Nœud pap et rouge à lèvres Sarl,
Cagnes sur Mer

ISBN: 978-2-9558790-2-3
Statutory deposit: November 2016

**This book was created in partnership with Orezza
and Zepter**

ANDREA MÄUSLI

Andrea Mäusli has been a culinary recipe creator and a food stylist for over 15 years in Switzerland.

PHILIPPE KUENTZ

Doctor Philippe Kuentz, ex athletic international, is doctor to the AS Monaco Football Club.

ELÉONORE SCHOETTEL

Eléonore Schoettel produces culinary shows on Swiss television.

EVE TIOLLIER

Eve Tiollier is the Doctor of Sciences and a dietitian. For more than 15 years she has provided nutrition consulting services for high level athletes in all different sports.

TARA OSTROWE

Tara Ostrowe, MS, RD, CSSD is a dietitian specializing in sports nutrition, and is responsible for the performance nutrition programs of the New York Football Giants and the New York Red Bulls. She also is responsible for the nutritional needs of the AS Monaco FC players.